Highlights

from these exciting times

A COLLECTION OF ARTICLES OF LASTING INTEREST FROM THE PAGES OF POPULAR MECHANICS MAGAZINE

Staff Editor:
Richard Harmet

Popular Mechanics Press

Library of Congress
Catalogue Card No. 59-9532

Preface

The world in which we live is bursting with excitement! Each day brings new developments in man's attempts to conquer space, to utilize the power unleashed by fission and fusion, to ease human suffering caused by disease and famine, to learn more about the universe in which we live. Scientific and technological advancements become more electrifying each day, and the possibilities for the future are beyond comprehension.

In our rapidly shrinking world, even the most remote areas are affected by and taking advantage of this progress. Through modern science and technology, these areas are making rapid progress in their attempts to catch up with the modern world.

Going hand in hand with these advancements is adventure. Behind the precision machinery are human beings, dedicated to the development of technological excellence. These adventurers range from laboratory scientists working on abstract research projects to drivers straining to get the last bit of speed from their racing cars. Even explorers and adventure seekers fall into this category, for today these rugged individuals rely heavily on their modern equipment. The experiences of all these men make stimulating reading.

Popular Mechanics Magazine is known the world over for keeping people informed on the latest happenings in the fields of science and technology. Its articles accent the *significance* of developments, thereby giving readers a better understanding and appreciation of the world in which we live, and a more accurate glimpse of the future.

Collected here are authoritative, adventure-packed articles on today's happenings, and responsible speculation on the world of tomorrow. These articles are truly *"Highlights from these exciting times."*

Contents

ALASKA —

FABULOUS FRONTIER

*Our 49th state has everything from traffic jams
to untamed wilderness. In Alaska you can hunt
bear in the morning, attend a symphony concert in
the evening, and play a round of golf at midnight.
It's 20th century technology and Wild West
frontier in a large economy package*

by Kenneth Anderson

The late general Billy Mitchell, who gained a niche in history by correctly forecasting the significance of air power, also made this prediction: "Whoever holds Alaska will hold the world."

Mitchell's canny insight showed him the future strategic importance of polar air routes. But the prediction had no more impact than a damp sponge on a window when he made it in 1935. Alaska then was believed by many people to be the legendary land of "Dangerous Dan McGrew" where sourdoughs scooped gold dust out of mountain streams and raced dog sleds across endless glaciers. At that time the total population of the territory, around 60,000 including Indians and Eskimos, would have made a city smaller than Terre Haute, Ind.

A generation later, as Alaska cuts its statehood teeth, a *cheechako*, or tenderfoot, would find this vast, last frontier has indeed become the keystone of global strategy that Billy Mitchell envisioned. Big Air Force bases have been established—Eielson and Ladd at Fairbanks and Elmendorf at Anchorage. Army units are stationed at Fort Richardson, Big Delta and at Port Whittier (where a single building recently was completed at a dollar cost approaching the original purchase price of Alaska). Navy installations are located at Kodiak Island, Adak and Fairbanks. Numerous radar units are scattered over the rugged terrain of this polar crossroads.

Every fourth person among the 213,000 residents of our 49th state is a military man or one of his dependents. Like the permanent citizens, they are fully aware of Alaska's vital security role. The former owners of this land, the Russians, have air and missile-launching bases just beyond the Bering Strait. At the Diomede Islands, the United States and the U.S.S.R. are separated by only 2.4 miles of water.

The United States acquired Alaska from Russia in 1867 for $7,200,000 in gold. Although the price of the area—as big as Texas, California and

Montana combined—amounted to only two cents an acre, the deal was bitterly opposed by many Congressional leaders. They thought the land was worthless.

According to history books, the Czar also considered Alaska a liability and had tried for nearly 12 years to peddle it. After the Crimean War started, the Czar feared that Great Britain might seize Alaska before it could be sold.

Americans, still licking the wounds of the Civil War, also objected to Russian demands that the payment be made in gold. Neither nation was aware that Alaska was loaded with mineral wealth. Since the Klondike strike of the 1890s, nearly $700,000,000 in gold has been taken out of Alaska. The streams and mines now yield $8,000,000 worth of gold each year. And there's still a bank in Nome that will cash a poke of gold dust!

Besides gold, Alaska has deposits of most of the 33 strategic and commercially valuable minerals, such as tin, mercury, chromium, copper, zinc, platinum, tungsten and antimony. Uranium production began in 1957 and a dozen oil companies have leased millions of acres for exploration. The first oil well is producing 900 barrels a day. A huge iron deposit has been found at Klukwan. And Alaskan coal mines yield about $7,000,000 worth of fuel a year. However, exploitation of Alaska's mineral wealth has lagged because of production costs in that region.

Wages are higher, too. But the Alaska Employment Security Commission does not encourage job seekers to travel to Alaska unless they have a "definite job commitment first." Some skilled workers may earn as much as seven dollars an hour in Alaska, but a recent survey showed that 12 percent of the state's labor force was unemployed. The only workers needed in Alaska, according to the commission, are certain professional and technical personnel in engineering and medicine.

In the larger cities, Alaska offers most of the comforts and conveniences of civilization. You can fly to Anchorage (which claims to

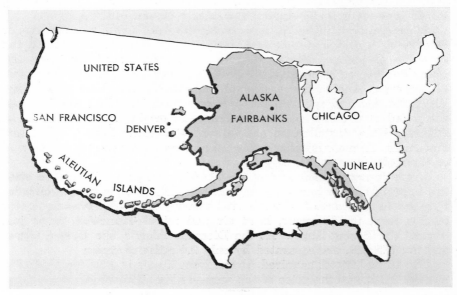

U. S. Forest Service photos

have more air traffic than Los Angeles, Cleveland or Dallas) on several commercial airlines. At the airport, you can pick up your choice of new cars from a rent-a-car service. And on a drive through the business district you might find yourself in a traffic jam.

Anchorage has more than 30,000 cars on its streets. And, as in the states to the south, many of the drivers are housewives on their way to a supermarket or a beauty shop. Or they may be returning to their homes in modern apartment buildings or contemporary-styled houses topped with TV antennas.

During the summer season, local citizens may be found sun-bathing at Lake Spenard, watching a tennis tournament or playing golf. In fact, Alaska has golf courses where you can play a match at midnight.

For intellectual-type pioneers, Anchorage has a symphony orchestra, a theater workshop, a $350,000 public library and "Great Books" discussion groups.

Education in the elementary and high schools is rated as good as or better than that offered in most stateside communities. Standard achievement tests show that reading skill of Anchorage pupils is as much as a year and a half ahead of national averages. Alaska has its own university at Fairbanks. Community colleges are operated at Anchorage, Ketchikan and Juneau. A multimillion-dollar Alaska Methodist College has been started at Anchorage.

Thriving modern cities at Alaska's northern latitudes are not unusual. By looking at a map of the world, you'll see that Ketchikan is farther south than Moscow, Glasgow, or Riga. Anchorage and Seward are about the same distance from the North Pole as Stockholm, Oslo, Leningrad, or Helsinki.

And, although Alaska has glaciers and winter temperatures of 70 below zero, all of the state isn't buried by ice and snow—even in the long dark nights of January. This newest state, if superimposed on a map of the other 48, would stretch from northern Minnesota to western Texas, with two "panhandles" stretching into southern California and Georgia.

As the climate of Minnesota differs from that of Texas and Georgia, so do the various sections of Alaska experience a wide range of climates. Fairbanks has recorded temperatures down to 66 degrees below zero, but in the panhandle areas the winter temperatures are no more severe than in many stateside communities above the Mason-Dixon line. Average January readings at Ketchikan, Sitka, Dutch Harbor and Atka are about 10 degrees warmer than those of the Chicago and Des Moines areas.

Summer temperatures in the 90s have been recorded in many Alaska communities. At Fort Yukon, on the Arctic Circle, the mercury once rose to 100 degrees. Rainfall ranges from a soggy 151 inches a year at Ketchikan to a semi-arid seven inches at Fort Yukon. Despite the weather extremes, Alaska apparently is a healthy state; it has the lowest death rate in the nation.

It's still possible to obtain a 160-acre farm in Alaska under the federal homestead law. But the pioneer farmer of today may find homesteading a formidable task. It takes a good-sized grubstake to establish a "quarter section" farm with modern equipment and living facilities in Alaska. When great-granddad developed his farm on the western prairies, he could get started with the tools and supplies he carried in his wagon and the animals that pulled it. To get started on an Alaska homestead, a farmer may have to buy or rent a bulldozer to clear the timber. And if he damages a couple of expensive farm machines on hidden roots or rocks, he may be out of business before his first crop is harvested.

Nevertheless, there is farm land available in Alaska and the state hopes eventually to produce half the food it needs. The growing season around Juneau, Ketchikan and Wrangell is as long as in much of the Midwest. Farther north, there are fewer frost-free days but, since the summer days are long, farmers are able to grow fabulous vegetable crops. Corn, tomatoes and tree fruits are about the only crops that will not mature in the short season.

The Federal government also will sell for as little as $2.50 an acre small tracts and homesites to persons who want to establish a resort, fur farm, poultry ranch or filling station.

Whether an Alaskan is watching a television show in Fairbanks, playing golf in Anchorage or milking cows on a Matanuska Valley farm, he cannot escape the frontier atmosphere. He may see parka-clad Eskimos in the city stores, kayaks skimming past moored seaplanes or totem poles behind radio towers. And he is always a short drive and a hike away from a wonderland of hunting and fishing.

Sportsmen who have lingered for hours over lines in the fished-out lakes of the older states would be startled by the catches Alaskans tote home from nearby streams—12-pound silver salmon, 16-pound rainbow trout and Chinook salmon that would crowd a home freezer.

A short trip from Anchorage puts the hunter within gunsight of moose, caribou, deer, bear, mountain goat and white Dall sheep. Inland game birds available include ptarmigan (20-per-day limit) and spruce hen. Mallard, teal and black brant inhabit the coastal waters and lakes.

The federally owned Alaska Railroad takes parties of hunters and fishermen on the morning run from Anchorage and drops them off near

Alaska's farm lands yield fabulous vegetable crops during the long summer days

Since the famous Klondike strike of the 1890's, more than $700 million worth of gold has been panned and mined in mineral-rich Alaska

their favorite spots. The sportsmen bag their bear or land their trout and return to the tracks in time to flag down the afternoon train returning from Fairbanks.

Hunters also make frequent use of the services of bush pilots for air trips to remote areas where they can shoot Canadian and snow geese, or perhaps polar bear. At least one airborne guide guarantees that his client will return with a pelt.

And Alaska has game to match its size. Record grizzly and brown-bear pelts are in the neighborhood of 11 feet in width. One bull moose had 25-point antlers with a spread of over six feet. Fishing records include a rainbow trout nearly 35 inches long.

Besides providing recreation and food for Alaskans, the state's fish and wildlife are important sources of income. Fishing is the biggest industry and fur is the third largest source of income, behind mining. Nearly 25,000 people work in Alaska's 100 commercial fisheries which annually produce millions of cases of canned salmon, plus herring, halibut, sablefish, shrimp, crabs and oysters.

The abundant fish supply also helps support Alaska's fur industry. The state has many licensed fur farmers who raise mink, blue fox and silver fox in captivity. (The Department of Interior suggests there is plenty of room for expansion of this type of enterprise in Alaska.) Fish is a basic food for fur-farm animals and it can be obtained cheaply in southeastern and coastal areas of the state.

Extensive timber resources can support future wood products, pulp and paper industries. The Tongass National Forest alone has over 78,000,000,000 feet of timber, mostly hemlock and spruce. There are forests of birch and other hardwoods in other parts of the state. A $5,000,000 pulp mill recently was established at Ketchikan.

Hydroelectric dams may eventually beef up Alaskan industries. A Bureau of Reclamation survey of about two-thirds of the state's 580,000 square miles showed there are about 200 likely spots for hydroelectric plants. It has been estimated that Alaska's vast water-power resources could be used to make 50,000,000,000 kilowatt hours of electricity— about three and a half times the annual output of Grand Coulee Dam.

Like its sister states, Alaska's geography is marked by names that spell out the history of the region. The name of Alaska, itself, is from the Aleut language and means "The Great Land." Chicagof, Baranof and Andreafsky are as Russian in origin as the onion-shaped church steeples in the Aleutian Islands. Prince William Sound and Prince of Wales Island show British influence while such places as El Capitan, Cordova and Valdez are tokens of Spanish conquests. Crooked Creek, Dime Landing, Fishhook, Cold Foot and Purgatory are reminders of the Gold Rush era.

The language of Alaskans also shows the influence of the Klondike period. If a miner talks about "flour," for example, he may be referring to gold dust rather than cake recipes. "Hi yu" is not a greeting but a Chinook expression meaning "plenty." A "strike" is an ore discovery and a "chuck" is a stream. A "mukluk" is something you wear on your feet but "muckamuck" is something you eat. And "mush" is a command to a dog team.

It's been a long haul for Alaska from the days when Russians who didn't want the land finally unloaded it on Americans who were almost equally unenthusiastic about the deal. For 45 years of its "poor relative" history it didn't even rate a territorial status. When statehood was first proposed, in 1916, even Alaskans laughed at the proposal. After World War II, however, the campaign finally gained enough momentum to clear the Congressional hurdle. But statehood supporters had a constant symbol of encouragement: The state flower is the forget-me-not.

ALASKA

AREA: 586,400 SQ. MILES   POPULATION: 213,000

CAPITAL: JUNEAU   GOVERNOR: WILLIAM A. EGAN

ORIGIN OF NAME: CORRUPTION OF A NATIVE WORD
MEANING "GREAT COUNTRY"

STATE FLOWER
FORGET-ME-NOT

STATE BIRD:
WILLOW PTARMIGAN

MAJOR PRODUCTS: FISH, LUMBER, PULP, GOLD, SILVER,
COPPER, LEAD, PLATINUM, COAL, MERCURY, ANTIMONY,
TIN, PETROLEUM, CHROMIUM, TUNGSTEN, FUR

1867 PURCHASE PRICE: $7,200,000

by Clifford B. Hicks

Versatile Lithium

This little-known metal has a wide variety of uses — from playing a vital part in H-bomb fusion to giving soda pop its tingly flavor

Pure lithium (left) is silvery white, can be cut with a knife

Chances are you've never even heard of a substance called Li-6. Most people haven't. But then most people hadn't heard of a substance called U-235 until an A-bomb flashed over Hiroshima in 1945. In the near future, Li-6 could just possibly be even more explosive in its impact on history than U-235. What is Li-6?

Li is the chemical symbol for lithium, an alkali metal which is the lightest of all solid elements. Until recently, lithium was looked on as the poor cousin of the other alkali metals, a ne'er-do-well actor who never would amount to much. Instead of the poor cousin, lithium may turn out to be the rich uncle who turns up unexpectedly to solve the family's problems.

Li-6 is one facet of lithium's personality. It is one of the natural isotopes of the element, just as U-235 is one form of uranium. There's a cloud of secrecy around the H-bomb, but a good guess is that the material in that bomb started out as Li-6. Furthermore, if current projects are successful in taming the H-bomb, Li-6 may play a key role in the fusion reactor.

Lithium not only is one of the key elements in nuclear science, but is solving problems in other fields. In this country we are using 10

times as much lithium as we did just five years ago. You use it countless times each day without recognizing it. Probably your car is
lubricated with lithium grease. The vitamin A you take in the morning
is manufactured with the aid of a lithium chemical. You may eat your
dinner off a plate glazed with lithium and take your bath in a tub coated
with lithium enamel. When you watch TV you're looking into lithium
glass.

Yet who ever heard of lithium? Perhaps you bumped into it in
high-school or college chemistry, but even here it was skimmed over in
the last five minutes of a class period devoted to more "important"
elements. Now the rich uncle, dressed in a cutaway coat, has come
home to join the family.

The fine clothes are there. In its pure metallic form lithium is a
beautiful silver-white. It weighs only one fifth as much as aluminum.
In water it floats like a cork, and you can cut it easily with a knife.

Li-6, when bombarded with neutrons, gives up tritium. This rare
triple-weight hydrogen probably is the stuff from which H-bombs are
made. The eminent physicist Hans Thirring has stated that fusion can
be maintained only with Li-6. One guess is that the H-bomb consists
of a small A-bomb (to initiate the reaction) surrounded by a thick
layer of Li-6 deuteride. Touch off the A-bomb in the center and you
get an explosion of stellar proportions.

Johann August Arvedson discovered the element in 1817, but it
remained strictly a laboratory curiosity until the 1880s, when one of
its compounds, lithium hydroxide, was used to boost the efficiency of
Edison storage batteries. Somewhat similar batteries powered submarines in World War I. Through the next several years it found its
way into carbonated drinks (it provided the tingly flavor) and in its

A vast array of belts carries lithium-rich ore through the processing plant

carbonate form as an ingredient for porcelain-enamel coatings—still its biggest use. It lowers the melting point of these enamels, making them flow more easily and permitting them to be fired at lower temperatures.

Then in 1931 a few atoms of lithium became the most important atoms in the world, though only the physicists recognized this at the time. Years before, Einstein in his classic equation had suggested that energy and mass are the same. In 1931, two physicists, Cockcroft and Walton, bombarded lithium with protons and found that alpha particles were ejected with tremendous energies. This energy, they found, was equivalent to the decrease in total mass. This was the first concrete evidence to support Einstein's theory and the first indication that energies of staggering magnitude could be released from the atom, a fact conclusively proved to the world 14 years later at Hiroshima.

In 1933, shortly after the Cockcroft and Walton experiment, a small firm in Philadelphia began producing lithium in an earthenware crock. Foote Mineral Company had once been in the business of supplying mineral specimens to collectors, and gradually had worked into the industrial field, supplying small quantities of little-known minerals, chemicals and metals. Virtually no one wanted lithium at that time, but Foote started turning out small batches anyway.

Today those batches have grown into freight-car loads and Foote is one of the three giants in the business. The others are American Potash and Chemical Corporation, and Lithium Corporation of America. Maywood Chemical Works is a smaller producer. All told, these firms turn out only about 100 tons of the pure metal per year, but they provide numerous lithium compounds in huge batches.

By far the biggest buyer is the Atomic Energy Commission, which recently signed a contract with the three major suppliers to take all the lithium hydroxide they can turn out. Certainly it is one of the strangest contracts ever drawn, for in effect it is based on a difference in the number of neutrons in lithium atoms.

Lithium in nature occurs as a combination of two stable isotopes, Li-6 and Li-7 (the latter has one more neutron). Less than 10 percent of all lithium is Li-6. These are the particular atoms the AEC wants,

Here a workman removes lithium concentrate from filters

and it has no known use for the others. But only the AEC can sort out the atoms, so it has to buy both types.

Though the separation method is secret, it would appear to be as easy as sorting golf balls from marbles compared to the incredibly difficult task of separating U-235 from U-28. In any event, once the atoms have been separated into two piles, the AEC has on hand a huge stack of Li-7 for which it has absolutely no use. According to the terms of the contract, only the original supplier can buy back this Li-7. Such a supplier then resells the material to anyone who wants it.

And many want it. It is this Li-7 that goes into the greases and TV tubes, the air conditioners and soft drinks. Lithium greases permit vehicles to operate in temperatures ranging from an icy minus-60 degrees to a scorching 130. In air conditioners, lithium chloride wrings water out of the air. Milady puts on lithium stearate when she covers her cheeks with face cream. Lithium compounds are used in bleaches and welding fluxes. They play a part in the production of antihistamines, vitamin A and synthetic rubber.

It's a good guess that lithium is also under test in two other booming fields. Missile fuels must have two things: The fuel itself and oxygen. Lithium compounds have a much higher oxygen content per weight than most other chemicals. Also, molten lithium metal would appear to be an excellent heat-transfer medium in nuclear reactors. The one drawback here is that at high temperatures lithium becomes extremely corrosive. With all these uses, it's apparent that more and more lithium will be needed. What about the supply?

Rich deposits are scattered around the world, and there seems to be plenty to go 'round. North America is believed to rank first. Canada has vast deposits and there's a "mountain of lithium" at King's Mountain, N. C. Africa probably ranks second, with a huge deposit at Bikita, Southern Rhodesia, generally conceded to be one of the world's outstanding deposits. There seems to be plenty of lithium-bearing ore in South America, Europe, Australia and Asia.

Wresting the lithium from the rock is not an easy job, and techniques vary somewhat. In one process, the ore is ground into fine sand and, through froth flotation, the lithium-rich particles are separated out. This material, about six percent lithium oxide, is mixed with limestone, and the mixture heated in a huge rotary kiln. The heat sets free lithium and potassium salts. From the resulting solution, lithium hydroxide is recovered by concentration and evaporation. In this process, lithium hydroxide is the end product which is shipped to the AEC.

It's a long road. About 230 pounds of raw ore must be processed to obtain a single pound of lithium, and of this pound only about 1½ ounces are Li-6, the real goal of the AEC.

Several projects are under way in this country — and presumably in others — for harnessing the energy of the hydrogen (fusion) bomb. It's barely possible that uranium (fission) reactors will be old hat before they ever come into style. If so, that dapper gentleman called lithium probably will be dictating the trend. No crystal ball is needed to foresee at least the possibility of a lithium-hydrogen age taking over before the age of the atom gets much of a start.

EIGHT MEMORABLE DAYS
IN THE

HISTORY of SPEED

A mile a minute, once dreamed of as the ultimate in speed, turned out to be only a starting point in the competition between men, their machines, and the clock

by Arthur R. Railton

Paintings by Robert Korta

Man likes to go fast. To some men, speed is a compulsion. Only overwhelming compulsion can explain why men sacrifice time, money and not infrequently, their lives for speed.

There are rewards, of course. But they don't match the risks. The one guarantee to the successful is the satisfaction of knowing that, temporarily at least, he is the world's fastest driver. For those who fail, there is nothing.

From the day man first put wheels under a platform, he has raced against his fellow men. When that platform became an automobile, he began racing the clock.

This was the start of the Golden Era of Speed—50 years of enormous achievement. It was only 50 years from December 1898 when Comte de Chasseloup-Laubat set the first record of 39.24 miles per hour, until September 1947 when John Cobb covered the mile at an average speed of 394.20 miles per hour.

Our history of speed begins on a road outside Paris where in December 1898 two pioneers began competing for the speed crown. Both, realizing the inadequacies of the gasoline engines of the era, put their faith in electricity.

After a series of alternating record-setting runs, Jenatzy came out victorious in April 1899 with a speed of 65.79 miles per hour, becoming the first person to drive a mile a minute (actually he was driving over a kilometer course and probably did not realize he had hit the magical mile-a-minute figure). His competitor, Chasseloup-Laubat, will be remembered as being the first speed-record holder, with his initial run of 39.24 miles per hour in the electric Jeantaud in December 1898.

Electricity gave way to steam in 1902 when Serpollet in a streamlined steamer averaged 75.06 miles per hour, nearly 10 miles faster than the fastest electric.

JENATZY 1899—60 miles per hour

The story of automotive speed begins in April 1899 when, on a road at Acheres, France, an electric-powered car driven by Frenchman Camille Jenatzy was the first to go a mile a minute, averaging 65.79 miles per hour for one kilometer.

RIGOLLY 1904—100 miles per hour

First to hit 100 was another Frenchman, M. Rigolly who, on July 21, 1904, in a four-cylinder, angular-bodied Gobron-Brillie averaged 103.56 miles per hour for one kilometer along a dusty road at Ostend, Belgium.

MARRIOTT 1906—120 miles per hour

First to go two miles a minute was American Fred Marriott who, on January 27, 1906, drove the sleek, unbelievably simple Stanley Steamer Rocket at 127.66 miles per hour for one mile along the hard sands at Daytona Beach, Florida.

DePAOLO 1925—100 miles per hour at Indianapolis

First to break 100 for the 500 miles of the famous Indianapolis Race was Pete De Paolo who averaged 101.13 miles per hour in a supercharged Duesenberg on May 30, 1925, beating out a Miller Junior Eight by less than a minute.

SEGRAVE 1926—Last of the Normals

On Southport sands, England, on March 17, 1926, H.O.D. Segrave hit 152.33 miles per hour in his four-liter Sunbeam V12, the last of the true racing cars to hold the record. After this, aircraft-engined, specialized giants took over.

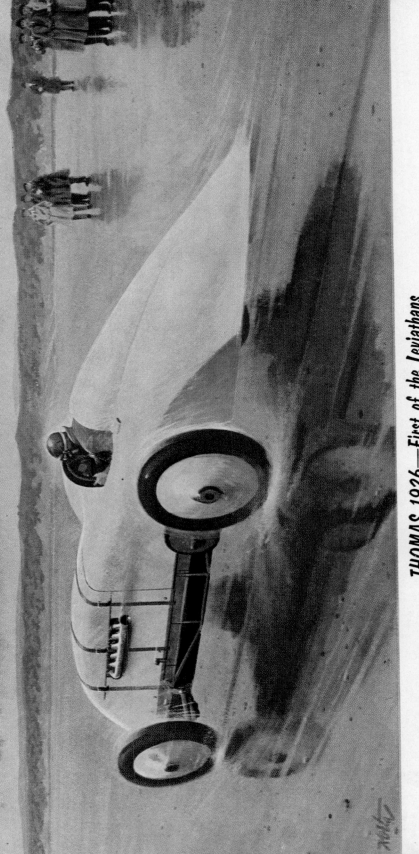

THOMAS 1926—First of the Leviathans

To begin the reign of the giants, Britisher Parry Thomas drove a record 171.02 miles per hour on a wet beach at Pendine, Wales. His car with its V12 Liberty aircraft engine had a displacement seven times larger than that of Segrave's.

CAMPBELL 1935—300 miles per hour

On the parched whiteness of Bonneville Salt Flats, Utah, Sir Malcolm Campbell became the first to go 300 miles per hour when he drove his 2500-horsepower aircraft-engined Blue Bird at a record 301.129 miles per hour September 3, 1935.

COBB 1947—400 miles per hour

John Cobb of England paces nervously as his Railton Special is readied for its speed runs at Bonneville, September 16, 1947. One run was timed at 403.14 miles per hour. His two-way average of 394.196 miles per hour is the present record.

It wasn't until August 1902 that the gasoline engine came into the picture. An American, W. K. Vanderbilt (in a European Mars car, however) went to Ablis, France, and raised the steamer's mark to 76.08 miles per hour. Gasoline remained king for three years through a succession of record-breaking runs that included one by Henry Ford in the Ford 999, a gearless, clutchless monster that hit 91.37 miles per hour on the ice at Lake St. Clair, Wis. Ford's speed fame was short-lived, however, as two weeks later Vanderbilt in a Mercedes raised the record to 92.30 miles per hour at Daytona.

Steam made its brief comeback when Fred Marriott in the Stanley Steamer Rocket, a fragile looking ultrastreamlined speedster, averaged 127.66 miles per hour at Daytona to become the first man to go two miles a minute.

In 1914 rules were established requiring that speed runs be made in two directions with the average of the two being the official speed.

By 1926 the speed record stood at 150.87 miles per hour, a record set by Malcolm Campbell in a Sunbeam. He had broken his own record to do it, a record of 146.16 miles per hour, both set at Pendine sands in Wales. Thus Campbell became the first man to average 150 miles per hour.

Sunbeam came through again when H. O. D. Segrave, in the smallest gasoline car ever to hold the record, set a new mark of 152.33 miles per hour at Southport, England. The engine represented a triumph of design, it being a V12 engine of only 244-cubic-inch displacement— smaller than any eight-cylinder engine built in an American production car today. The Segrave car was no special car—it was a practical racing vehicle, the last of the normal cars to hold the record. From here on, the emphasis was on specialized cars with aircraft engines, cars designed to go extremely fast in a straight line for a short distance.

The first of this parade of monsters was the Liberty-aircraft-engine Higham Special driven by J. G. P. Thomas. It boosted the speed mark to 169.20 and started the record zooming upward after years of gradual increases.

Despite the fact that the Liberty engine wasn't running right, Thomas easily smashed all existing speed records. The lesson was clear —to those interested—the way to set records was to get a tremendous engine and put it on wheels. Aircraft engines became the typical choice.

The following day Thomas ran through the mile again and raised the record to 171.4 miles per hour despite an extremely wet beach. The Liberty engine had a 27,059-cubic-centimeter displacement (1650 cubic inches), almost seven times more than the Sunbeam whose record it broke.

From here on, the record climbed sharply. By 1927, the speed merchants discovered that the hard sand at Daytona was best for their runs. Segrave brought a twin-engined 1000-horsepower Sunbeam to the Florida beach and boosted the mark to 203.79 miles per hour, becoming the first to break the double-century barrier.

In the following year, 1928, three drivers made the pilgrimage to Daytona: Lockhart's previously mentioned and ill-fated Stutz; Keech's three-engined Triplex special, a tremendous car of great power and little engineering; and Campbell's Napier-engined Special. Campbell set the new record at 206.96 miles per hour. A few months later Ray

Keech, an American, in the crude Triplex-White Special, raised it to 207.55.

The following year, March 1929, Segrave returned to Daytona in a Napier-aircraft-engine car, the Golden Arrow, and boosted the record sharply to 231.36 miles per hour, an achievement which won him a knighthood when he returned to England.

Malcolm Campbell then began a series of record-breaking runs which gave him a monopoly on the mark until 1937. In 1931, 1932, 1933 and 1935, Campbell set new records. Finally at Bonneville he became the first to hit 300 miles per hour with an average of 301.13. This marked the ninth time that Campbell (by this time he was Sir Malcolm) had held the speed record—an achievement unmatched by anyone else.

The following year, Eyston raised his record to 345.5 miles per hour. A month later, September 1938, the Railton Special driven by J. R. Cobb took the crown from the Thunderbolt with a speed of 350.2 miles per hour.

Later the same month Eyston came back to break Cobb's mark and raise the record to 357.50 miles per hour. The following August, Cobb regained the crown with an average of 369.70 miles per hour.

There the record stood until after World War II when Cobb returned to Bonneville in his same Railton Special and, for the first time in history, drove a vehicle over land at a speed of more than 400 miles per hour. On his south-to-north run, he averaged 403.14 miles per hour. His north-to-south run was 385.65 miles per hour, for a two-way average of 394.20 miles per hour, the present world's record.

WORLD'S LAND-SPEED RECORDS

One Direction Only

Date	Driver	Car	Place	M. P. H.
Dec. 1898	Chasseloup-Laubat	Jeantaud	France	39.24
Jan. 1899	Jenatzy	Jenatzy	France	41.42
Jan. 1899	Chasseloup-Laubat	Jeantaud	France	43.69
Jan. 1899	Jenatzy	Jenatzy	France	49.92
Mar. 1899	Chasseloup-Laubat	Jeantaud	France	57.60
Apr. 1899	Jenatzy	Jenatzy	France	65.79
Apr. 1902	Serpollet	Serpollet	France	75.06
Aug. 1902	Vanderbilt	Mors	France	76.08
Nov. 1902	Fournier	Mors	France	76.60
Nov. 1902	Augieres	Mors	France	77.13
July 1903	Rigolly	Gobron-Brillie	Belgium	83.47
Nov. 1903	Duray	Gobron-Brillie	France	84.73
Jan. 1904	Ford	Ford 999	Wisconsin	91.37
Jan. 1904	Vanderbilt	Mercedes	Daytona	92.30
Mar. 1904	Rigolly	Gobron-Brillie	France	94.78
May 1904	de Caters	Mercedes	Belgium	97.25
July 1904	Rigolly	Gobron-Brillie	Belgium	103.55
Nov. 1904	Baras	Darracq	Belgium	104.52
Jan. 1905	Macdonald	Napier	Daytona	104.65
Dec. 1905	Hemery	Darracq	France	109.65
Jan. 1906	Marriott	Stanley	Daytona	127.66
Mar. 1910	Oldfield	Benz	Daytona	131.72

Two Directions

Date	Driver	Car	Place	M. P. H.
June 1914	Hornsted	Benz	England	124.10
May 1922	Guinness	Sunbeam	England	133.75
July 1924	Thomas	Delage	France	143.31
July 1924	Eldridge	Fiat	France	146.01
Sept. 1924	Campbell	Sunbeam	Wales	146.16
Mar. 1926	Campbell	Sunbeam	Wales	150.87
Mar. 1926	Segrave	Sunbeam	England	152.33
Apr. 1926	Thomas	Thomas Special	Wales	169.30
Apr. 1926	Thomas	Thomas Special	Wales	171.02
Feb. 1927	Campbell	Napier-Campbell	Wales	174.88
Mar. 1927	Segrave	Sunbeam	Daytona	203.79
Feb. 1928	Campbell	Napier-Campbell	Daytona	206.96
Apr. 1928	Keech	Triplex-White	Daytona	207.55
Mar. 1929	Segrave	Irving-Napier	Daytona	231.44
Feb. 1931	Campbell	Napier-Campbell	Daytona	246.09
Feb. 1932	Campbell	Napier-Campbell	Daytona	253.97
Feb. 1933	Campbell	Campbell Special	Daytona	272.46
Mar. 1935	Campbell	Campbell Special	Daytona	276.82
Sept. 1935	Campbell	Campbell Special	Bonneville	301.13
Nov. 1937	Eyston	Thunderbolt	Bonneville	312.00
Aug. 1938	Eyston	Thunderbolt	Bonneville	345.50
Sept. 1938	Cobb	Railton	Bonneville	350.20
Sept. 1938	Eyston	Thunderbolt	Bonneville	357.50
Aug. 1939	Cobb	Railton	Bonneville	369.70
Sept. 1947	Cobb	Railton	Bonneville	394.20

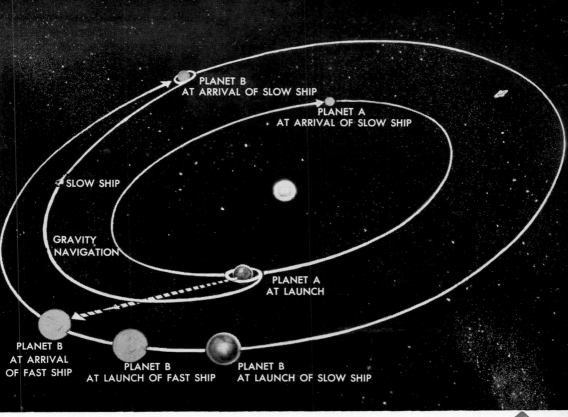

PLANET B
AT ARRIVAL OF SLOW SHIP

PLANET A
AT ARRIVAL OF SLOW SHIP

SLOW SHIP

GRAVITY
NAVIGATION

PLANET A
AT LAUNCH

PLANET B
AT ARRIVAL
OF FAST SHIP

PLANET B
AT LAUNCH OF FAST SHIP

PLANET B
AT LAUNCH OF SLOW SHIP

The drawing above shows the difference between slow and fast-ship navigation

NAVIGATING IN SPACE

A discussion of the problems of space navigation by Dr. Peter A. Castruccio, Advisory Engineer for Missile Guidance and Space Communications for Westinghouse

Man will conquer space. He will travel to the moon, and to other planets in our solar system.

But if he is to succeed in this most dramatic of all human undertakings, he must first solve two great problems. I believe we can reasonably expect solutions to both.

The first of these problems, of course, is to develop power plants powerful enough to push him out into the vastness of space and return him to earth. Travel in space itself requires relatively little power; most of the energy must be spent in overcoming the gravitational pull of the earth, and of the moon or other bodies which man has the daring to explore. This initial push requires so much power that today's power plants are barely equal to the task. Not much power is left available for actual space travel.

For this reason we must use to the utmost any natural forces which are available — fortunately, powerful sources are available. We can take advantage of these forces in a method known as "gravity navigation."

Imagine, for a moment, that there is a spaceship traveling around the sun at the same speed as the earth travels around the sun. Two forces act on this ship: The pull of the sun and the centrifugal force of the ship's motion. These forces are exactly equal; the ship neither falls toward the sun nor escapes outward. Now imagine that we add a gentle push in the same direction the ship is traveling. The ship speeds up, its centrifugal force increases, and exceeds the inward pull of the sun. This causes the orbit of the ship to become elongated. The ship now follows an ellipse or oval route through space. The secret of gravity navigation lies simply in making the furthest point of the ellipse coincide with the planet we wish to reach.

Without question we can and will use this system of gravity navigation in the near future. We'll make the trip in two steps. First, the ship will vanquish the pull of the earth by acquiring sufficient speed (some 18,000 miles per hour) to orbit around the earth. As an earth satellite, of course, it will be moving, with the same speed as the earth, around the sun. Next we'll give it a relatively gentle push at precisely the right instant and in precisely the right direction to send it out on an elliptical orbit around the sun. If the push is exactly right, it will carry the ship to one of the planets, which also is orbiting around the sun. Thus we can use the speed of the earth as a "springboard to space."

Obviously this method is time consuming. The speed of travel is limited, and we must wait possibly months or years for the planets to assume their proper positions for such a voyage. We are in much the same situation as the ancient sailing master, who had to await favorable tides and whose speed was limited by the strength of the wind in the sails.

But as power plants become more powerful, space travel will gradually become faster. Eventually gravity navigation will yield to straight-line powered navigation.

The second of the two great problems to be solved is the problem of guiding a spaceship to its destination. Because we'll expend most of the ship's energy for the trip, little will remain to correct the guidance of the craft. Thus the initial "aim" of the craft must be extremely accurate; the more precise the guidance, the less fuel we'll waste.

Let's look at the guidance problem for a moment. Guidance depends upon navigation, which is simply the art of going from point A to point B. On the earth's surface, both A and B (for example New York and Chicago) are determined by two things: Latitude and longitude. When you navigate on earth, you simply determine the latitude and longitude of your vehicle (be it plane, ship or even car), and you can easily calculate the direction you must travel to arrive at the longitude and latitude of your point of destination. You can even become temporarily lost and still reach your destination, because A and B do not move with respect to each other.

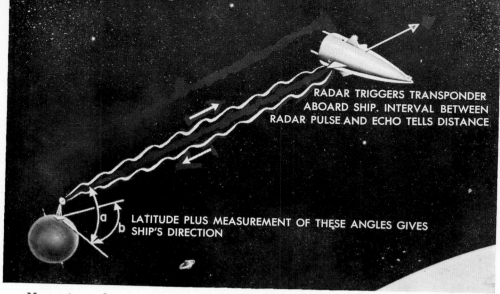

RADAR TRIGGERS TRANSPONDER ABOARD SHIP. INTERVAL BETWEEN RADAR PULSE AND ECHO TELLS DISTANCE

LATITUDE PLUS MEASUREMENT OF THESE ANGLES GIVES SHIP'S DIRECTION

Measuring radar signals and their echoes determines the course of the spaceship

Not so in space. Both A and B move because all planetary bodies move with respect to each other. Therefore your destination doesn't stand still. It's as though you were on a motor trip to Chicago, and Chicago kept moving all the time you were on the road.

In addition to this difficulty of a moving destination, travel in space occurs in three dimensions instead of the two (latitude and longitude) of your travel on earth. Actually, we can say that navigation in space is four-dimensional: Three space dimensions and one time dimension. Because the speed of planets is very great (67,000 miles per hour for earth, 54,000 for Mars and 79,000 for Venus), even a slight error in timing and speed may cause a complete miss. And if you miss, you very likely will wander through space forever.

That's the problem. Now there are two methods we can use to guide a ship through space. We can give it precise speed and direction initially, as if it were shot from a gun. Or we can launch it with a reasonable degree of accuracy, and correct the course subsequently during the flight. The first is called the "ballistic" method. Hitting Mars ballistically is about as easy as shooting a swallow from half a mile away with an arrow.

The second method, known as midcourse guidance, is the most practical and also the most reliable because it allows for continuous correction of errors in the trajectory.

In order to use midcourse guidance, we must know certain facts: The ship's position, the ship's speed, the ship's direction of travel and the "future position" of the destination at the expected moment of arrival.

The last of these facts—the position of a planet at a given moment —we know very accurately from astronomical tables.

Two of the remaining facts—the ship's position and speed—can be determined from within the ship, or by observing the ship from the earth and relaying the information to the ship. One practical solution is to have the ship tracked by radar on earth. Each radar impulse from earth triggers a "transponder" on the ship, which answers with a powerful radio impulse. The time interval between the radar pulse and its echo can be used to determine the distance of the ship from the earth.

Using the same system, we can measure the speed of the ship. Have you ever waited for a train at a crossing and listened to its whistle? Just as the train passes, the sound seems to drop in pitch. This is known as the "Doppler effect." Here's what happens: Because the train is moving, you in effect are "running away" from the train's whistle and its sound waves. Therefore you receive fewer waves, and the pitch of the whistle seems to drop. The same phenomenon applies to radio waves. The frequency drops as the receiver moves away from the transmitter, and increases as it moves toward the transmitter. By measuring this change in frequency we can determine the ship's speed.

Actually, for a really accurate speed measurement we need three different "speed fixes" from three different radars on the earth's surface. We can determine the ship's direction by measuring the angles. One angle is the latitude of the transmitter itself. The other two show the azimuth and elevation with respect to the earth's surface. Thus the radar-beacon system will yield three facts: The ship's distance, its direction and its speed.

Another method is for the crew of the ship itself to determine its position. All it needs is a "frame of reference." In this method we select the sun as the basis of the frame of reference, and also three stars. The navigator draws a line from each star to the center of the sun. His fourth line is from the ship's position to the sun, and he determines this by measuring the angles from the other three lines. So far, all he knows is that the ship lies somewhere along this fourth line. Now he measures the apparent diameter of the sun, and he can determine his distance from it, thus completely fixing his position. The only remaining fact he needs is his speed and he can determine this, once again, by the Doppler effect, which causes the shift of certain components of the stars' light.

So far we have been concerned with the precise position of the ship in space, its speed and course. Now that we have this information, what do we do with it? We feed it into computers to calculate whether there are any errors in the "orbit" or course of the ship and, if so, what corrections we must make.

Now we transmit these corrections to the ship for action. But here we face even further difficulties. We can't turn the ship like we do an airplane, simply because there is no air to act upon control surfaces. We can alter direction only by firing side rockets. We can alter speed only by firing tail or nose rockets.

But in doing this, still another difficulty arises. How can you impart a precise amount of side thrust when the ship itself may be moving backward, sideways or even tumbling and spinning along its course? Obviously to perform any correction you must first straighten out the ship along the ship-radar line of sight.

Again there are numerous ways we can solve the problem. One rather simple method is to use the radar pulse itself. If you dip your finger in a tub of water, you cause circular ripples to expand outward across the two-dimensional surface. Similarly, if you send a radar wave through three-dimensional space, the wave travels outward in an ever-

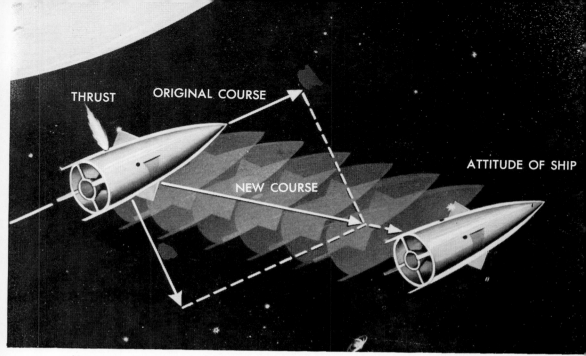

THRUST ORIGINAL COURSE

NEW COURSE

ATTITUDE OF SHIP

By using rockets, a spaceship may change its course (above) and its attitude

expanding sphere. We can take advantage of this. We mount four different antennas, which pick up the signals in phase, on the rear of the ship. When all four are equal, the ship is oriented on a direct line from the radar. If the phases are unequal, the ship can be straightened out by spinning masses, much like flywheels, inside the vessel.

Next the ship is rotated around its axis to bring the correcting side rocket into the proper position. Then the rocket is fired for the proper length of time. Subsequently other checks of the ship's position and trajectory must be made, and other corrections ordered if necessary, throughout the trip.

One of the big difficulties of such trips will be the effect of the enormous distances on communications. You can't pick up a radio telephone, say "Hello," and expect to get a prompt answer. Radio waves travel at a speed of 186,000 miles per second. Even at this speed, communicating with a spaceship in an orbit around Mars will be time consuming. For example, when Mars is at its closest approach to earth, it will still take a good 4½ minutes for a message to be received after it has been transmitted. Obviously there seems little point in a telephone conversation in which the initial "Hello" is answered nine minutes or even nine hours later. It is a fair bet that interplanetary messages will be telegraphic rather than voice, and that great emphasis will be placed on condensing the "message" into as few words as possible.

There is little doubt in my mind that man, now that he has succeeded in attaining escape velocities with his rockets, will himself escape from his mother planet and, using the immutable forces of nature to control and guide him, set off to explore his solar system.

STAIRWAY

The St. Lawrence Seaway, by making navigable the waterways between Lake Superior (elevation 602 feet) and the St. Lawrence River (sea level), has opened the Great Lakes' ports to ocean-going ships

by Richard F. Dempewolff

For the past four years, a Canadian-American army of mud-begrimed men in hard hats, numbering at times up to 22,000, has been digging a king-size ditch. To the clatter of jackhammers, the rumble of more than 150 giant shovels and draglines, and the roar of an endless stream of earthmovers, they have ground deep into the ancient bedrock beneath a brawling 180-mile section of the St. Lawrence River. Behind miles of protective dikes and cofferdams, their clanking steel monsters have gouged out footings for a string of big dams, massive concrete locks and many super powerplants.

This spring, when the last of the mud settled in the miles of canyon-like channels they carved, and the last raw earth embankment healed under a new hide of turf, the St. Lawrence Seaway became a Gargantuan $1,090,000,000 reality.

Unlike the 50-mile Panama Canal and the 100-mile Suez, the world's third great inland seaway (built jointly by the United States and Canada) is a two-fisted giant. The mighty dams that back up its rapids into usable waterways also harness the once-wild river, steering it through batteries of sluice gates in two big power dams. One of these is second only to Grand Coulee. From its rumbling generators,

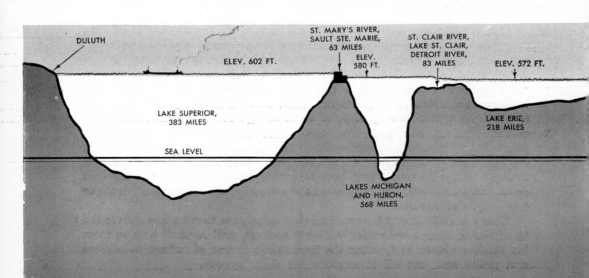

to the SEA

1,800,000 kilowatts of electricity can be fed into the power grids of Canada and the United States.

No less dramatic in its implications is the waterway created by the great dams. For the first time, deep-draft ocean ships are able to sail 2370 miles from the Atlantic to the heart of North America. Midwestern cities fringing the Great Lakes' 8300 miles of shoreline will become true seaports. Cities like Chicago, Duluth, Milwaukee, Detroit, Cleveland and Toronto are destined to become world ports. You may climb aboard a passenger liner at Chicago and sail to Liverpool, Bremerhaven, Cherbourg, Singapore—or where you will. The Dutch-owned Fjell-Orange Line already has launched one passenger-cargo liner, with accommodations for 110, for the Great Lakes trade. Another is on the ways. Fare? About $180 to Europe one way, they say.

You get some inkling of the staggering size of this project when you realize that the engineers had to devise a way to lift an ocean liner the height of a 60-story skyscraper, for Lake Superior sits 602 feet above the Atlantic. The St. Lawrence River and its Great Lakes headwaters, draining a land mass greater than Britain and France, make this drop in a series of steps like the cascading water in a tiered fountain. What the Seaway does is climb over those tiers on a series of great locks—huge "stairs" with water for treads.

Coming in from the Atlantic, a ship steams up the broad Gulf of St. Lawrence and into the narrowing river as far as Montreal. Two miles below the Jacques Cartier bridge, the skipper nudges his bow into a broad channel on the north side of the river. Massive 35-ton miter gates yawn to admit his vessel into St. Lambert and Cote St. Catherine Locks — first two steps in the giant staircase. Like all the

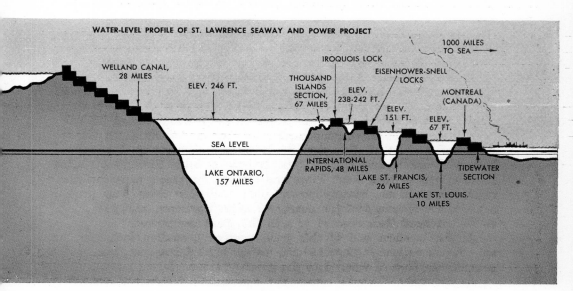

WATER-LEVEL PROFILE OF ST. LAWRENCE SEAWAY AND POWER PROJECT

Some key points in the Seaway: 1. Wiley-Dondero Canal; 2. Long Sault Dam; 3. Barnhart Island; 4. Robert H. Saunders-St. Lawrence Generating Station and the Robert Moses Power Dam (the U.S. half); 5. Cornwall, Ontario, and 6. the old Cornwall Canal

steps in the new waterway, these locks measure 800 feet long, 80 feet wide, with 30 feet of water over the sills. Allowing minimum clearance, a ship 768 feet long, 75 feet abeam and drawing 27 feet of water can squeeze in.

In two 25-foot leaps the ship clears Lachine Rapids. Sailing up a broad pool in the river called Lake St. Louis, the ship moves westward toward Beauharnois Locks, which hoist the vessel 84 feet to the level of a broad canal, carved in solid rock, that feeds Beauharnois Power Dam. On this pond the ship glides into another broad stretch of river—Lake St. Francis. Up to this point, the new system is entirely Canadian-built.

Fifty miles upstream the ship signals for clearance at the Bertrand H. Snell and Dwight D. Eisenhower Locks, on the American side. These two hydraulic elevators perform a 90-foot lift previously accomplished by 11 separate locks between the foot of International Rapids and the town of Iroquois, on the old Cornwall Canal that once accommodated small lake steamers. The old canals, locks and even the rapids themselves, lie deep under the placid water of a new lake, formed by water backed up behind mountainous piles of concrete—Long Sault Control Dam and Robert H. Saunders-St. Lawrence Generating Station and Robert Moses Power Dam. These bulwarks, built through the combined efforts of New York State and Ontario Province, form the heart of the international seaway power giant. Between them they pile up a placid navigation pool for nearly 40 miles upstream, and use the 81 to 90-foot head thus created to spin the giant generators.

At the western end of this pool, another Canadian lock lifts the ship five more feet to Ontario-level waters behind Iroquois Dam, which controls the flow of water into the great power pool.

Across Lake Ontario comes the spectacular 327-foot heave. This is accomplished in Canada's 28-mile Welland Canal, bypassing the Niagara River with its falls and gorge. Four single locks, a flight of three double locks and one guard lock do the job. Opened in 1932 to replace a century-old 14-foot-deep canal, the present locks and channels have been deepened to conform with the new Seaway specifications.

Once atop the Welland, a ship has navigated all of the official Seaway. The Soo Locks, providing the final lift into Lake Superior at Sault Ste. Marie, form the top step in the long stairway. But all through the Great Lakes big dredges, working under U. S. Army Engineers, are busy deepening harbors and interlake channels to the Seaway's official 442-foot bottom width and 27-foot depth. Target date for the last of this work is 1962.

Locking through the Seaway is swift and efficient.

"We cleared a backlog of 109 ships in the first 48 hours of operation," Norman Ashley will tell you. Ashley is one of the lock control operators on the 3½-mile Wiley-Dondero Canal linking Eisenhower and Snell. "The Canadians up at Iroquois figured we'd be a bottleneck because of our inexperience with this type lock, but it turned out we kept them hustling. We've lifted ships the entire 45 feet in six minutes at this lock. On the old canal half that lift took 15 to 20 minutes."

In a glass-enclosed blockhouse, jutting from the lock's broad apron like an airport control tower, Ashley operates the great miter gates and flood valves at a console of lights and switches. "Everything works in sequence," he points out. "If the big boom isn't down, I won't get a circuit okay to close the gates. If the gates aren't closed properly, I won't get a clear circuit to open the valves."

At his big board, Ashley watches as a lake-bound freighter enters the down-stream gate and sails into the cavernous lock chamber in which water has been dropped to downstream level. Actually, the new locks can take two lake steamers with room to spare. "A cabin cruiser wants to come through—let him in," Ashley suddenly shouts over an intercom to the downstream control operator.

"Those small-boat skippers," he explains, "are sometimes scared to come in with a big ship for fear they'll get banged all over the lock by water rushing in as the lock fills. Even in the Panama locks that happens. Here you'll hardly see a ripple as she comes up. Watch that little boat slip a bight over the floating bollard—that's all the mooring she needs."

The bollard, one of the new lock's innovations, is a floating mooring post that slides up a vertical track in the wall as water rises in the lock.

With both vessels tied up, Ashley and the downstream operator begin to throw switches in orderly sequence. The massive gates swing shut. Outside in the downstream canal, a huge girder lowers across the channel like a railroad crossing gate. "Each gate is protected by a fender like that," said Ashley. "It will stop an ocean freighter traveling at four knots."

Down below the control house, two giant whirlpools form outside the upstream gate as a pair of intake valves opens and gravity sucks a roaring torrent down through 15 by 16-foot culverts running through the sidewalls of the lock. Deep in the lock chamber, the mirror-like surface of the water creeps up the footage markers, faster and faster.

Secret of the smooth lift, according to L. W. Angell, chief engineer

This tunnel allows traffic to drive beneath the Eisenhower Lock on Wiley-Dondero Canal

for the seaway project, is a tricky system of intake ports. Instead of shooting straight up from the bottom, as it does in older locks, the rising water is fed through culverts in the sidewalls and shoots out into the 85-foot-deep lock bottom. Side ports from these transverse mains face each other, so that the water's tremendous energy is expended against itself. "We ran model tests that told us we had a good system," says Angell.

Going downstream, ships enter a full lock, and the water is dumped through outlet ports at the lower end.

Looking at the towering level of water outside the sheet of steel upstream of an empty lock, you can't help wondering what would happen if a ship should rupture that gate and let the whole upper St. Lawrence roar down the valley.

Not likely, according to Angell. The outside fenders protect that side of the big gate from ships. "Inside," he reveals, "two more fenders lying across the lock bottom lift up fore and aft of the ship to protect the gates from sharp prows and stern projections. This accounts for the fact that a 768-foot ship is the longest you can put into the 800-foot lock chamber. The difference is safety clearance."

That's not all. On the upriver side of Eisenhower Lock, facing the huge power pool, there's a superbackstop—a 350-ton vertical lift gate sunk in a deep slot in the massive concrete sill. "It will raise itself hydraulically," says Angell, "right through a full head of water roaring into the lock."

On top of that, beside each gate stands a crane and a pile of "stop-logs"—28-ton steel panels that can be dropped into emergency slots.

The new Seaway between Montreal and Ontario climbs through a total of seven locks, instead of 21, as on the old canal.

Exactly 210,515,000 yards of earth had to be moved to make way for the giant seaway. If you piled it all on a football field, that much dirt would reach 25 miles in the air. Or, as M. W. Oettershagen, Deputy Administrator for the Seaway, puts it: "you could haul it away in 60,000 trainloads of 100 cars each."

None of it was easy. Paul Bunyan's fabled deeds pale beside some of the tales that are bandied about Massena, N. Y., the heart of activity. Canadian contractors on the Beauharnois Canal had to gouge their two-mile channel—to standard seaway depth of 30 feet—through solid rock so tough it wrecked the best steel drills in eight hours. Kerosene torches burning at 4000 degrees were used to soften it so blast holes could be sunk.

To make room for the new power lake that would flood 38,000 acres in the International Rapids section, seven complete Canadian towns were moved, lock, stock and tavern on the backs of gigantic, multitired house-moving flatbed trucks; 42 miles of highway and 35 miles of railway had to be relocated; 21 miles of dikes had to be built to contain the new waterway.

Many contractors faced problems they'll never forget. Canadians, working through the crackling northern winters, had to blast great ice floes that threatened cofferdams; their fresh-poured concrete had to be kept under a barrage of steam jets to keep it from freezing. In summer, dredge operators, who had to work in white-water rapids, cabled their barges to bedrock ashore, or tied on to great blocks of concrete on the bottom to keep from being swept away.

On June 30, 1957, everything nearly went galley-west when a hurricane's low-pressure eye literally tipped Lake Ontario backward, so that its water was several feet higher downstream than upstream! Bob Connors, one of Matejka's engineers, had the headache of facing all that water as it roared down from Iroquois on a wild night that knocked out all communications. Using radio cars to report water levels upstream, his gantries were still inching up gates in the unfinished Long Sault Control Dam when the wall of water hit Massena. "We barely got enough gates open," he says. "The level at Massena went to 204.4 feet—just 1½ inches from flooding the Cornwall canals."

In spite of it all, the St. Lawrence was harnessed on schedule. "April 1, 1958 was deadline day for removal of the cofferdams at the powerhouse," says Matejka. "And on April first the last pile was pulled. May first was scheduled for commencing closure of rail and road access gaps in the dikes, and on that day we began pulling spikes. July one was set for the pool raising, and that was the day we blasted."

Today visitors can stand on any one of a dozen parks and sites, carved out of the river's lush banks and scenic islands, and look out on the inspiring sight of some 250,000 gallons per second of tumbling white spray as it roars from the two dams' batteries of sluices, marching across nearly two miles of river. Along the top of the 167-foot-high power dam, mammoth gantries, resembling four-legged stools for some giant to sit on, rumble along tracks atop the dam crest, raising and lowering gates to adjust the flow through the 32 big turbines (half for Canada, half for the U. S.) buried deep in concrete.

Everything you see is living proof of what the administrators cheer as an historic example of international cooperation.

To archeologists it was an important pile of dirt. According to Dr. Douglas Osborne, University of Washington archeologist who directed the Wakemap project, the mound was by far the choicest site in the region—the only stone-age site showing a long-term occupation uncovered in the Northwest.

About 1500 years ago a tribe of primitive people built a community on the north bank of the Columbia River 85 miles upstream from present-day Portland. Their descendants occupied this settlement until perhaps A. D. 1750. Through these centuries the rubble and refuse from their everyday activities accumulated in layers, eventually forming a broad, earthen mound.

In 1957 the University of Washington completed a five-year excavation of that mound. What they found gave scientists a complete chronology of the Northwest's prehistory, for Wakemap was an archeological timetable.

The excavators labored against time, knowing that very soon the gates of the new Dalles Dam three miles downstream were to be closed, flooding an eight-mile stretch of the river canyon behind it.

Last Look at a Forgotten Civilization

Archeologists worked against time to unearth artifacts from a 1500-year-old civilization before the Columbia River canyon was flooded by a dam reservoir

By John Burroughs

The first whites exploring the Northwest noticed the Wakemap mound. Lewis and Clark reached the mid-Columbia in the autumn of 1805. After portaging their equipment around Celilo Falls, they eased down the treacherous rapids below, where the river roared through restricted channels between outcroppings of volcanic basalt. Captain Clark noted: ". . . this place being verry bad I sent by land all the men who could not Swim . . . and proceeded down with the canoes two at a time to a village of 20 wood houses in a Deep bend to the Stard. Side . . . they are scattered permiscuisly on a elivated Situation near a mound of about 30 feet above the Common Leavel, which mound has some remains of houses and has every appearance of being artificial."

It was Wakemap mound, only recently abandoned.

A half-century later, pioneers traveling the Oregon Trail along the south bank of the river reported that Celilo Falls and the rapids below were the best fishing ground in the West. Indian tribes came hundreds of miles to spear and net enormous catches of ocean salmon. To these Indians, Wakemap was a mystery.

In 1925 a team from the University of California, making an archeological survey of the area, dug test pits in the mound. They concluded that the site should be looked into.

But nothing was done until 1952, when construction crews began work on the Dalles Dam. Excavation fell to the University of Washington under a contract from the National Park Service. First, the top of the mound was bulldozed. The resulting flat was staked off in five-foot squares, and each square assigned to a pair of diggers. Students from the university did most of the shovel work. They sifted every cubic inch of dirt. Each artifact recovered was catalogued and its exact location plotted with scaled diagrams. Three rows of adjacent squares, 100 feet in length, were dug to bedrock. They gave representative data.

The uncovered artifacts reflected the progress of Wakemap's inhabitants. Stone, antler and whalebone objects found in the deeper strata were crudely worked implements. The utensils and tools from the higher, later strata were carefully carved examples of fine craftsmanship. In the topmost strata the diggers found many ornamental objects.

The diggers also discovered other promising locations nearby. In one, bits of human bone protruded from the earth. Investigation uncovered a series of round pits about eight feet in diameter, which at some early period had been used for food storage and in later centuries for cremation. Clinkers in the incinerated material proved to be some of the finest carvings discovered.

Other sites turned up. A radioactive-carbon test on organic material found on the other side of the river indicated that the canyon had been inhabited 9000 years ago. Tentative dating for the lower strata of the mound itself was established—about 1500 years old.

Crews arrived to blast off some of the many primitive rock carvings, or petroglyphs, chipped in the basalt canyon walls. The blocks of rock, some of them weighing 20 tons, were removed to museums.

In the final weeks, amateur archeologists from the Oregon Archeological Society pitched in to help. They kept what they found, with the university reserving the right to photograph and catalogue significant artifacts.

The deadline arrived. A dam engineer pushed a button. Four hours later the new Lake Celilo was 60 feet deep.

Archeologists believe that these primitive pictures found near Wakemap represent Indian guardian spirits

Paints, from across the aisle. "We're sharing with Filipino capital, too. Can't meet our growing market from the States."

Down in the lounge I met Neldon Hoyt of L. D. Seymour, making a host of once-imported items. An electrical contractor told of contracts swamping his and other firms—$30,000,000 in new textile mills, three big drug plants, tire plants for the Big Three of rubber, to handle Philippine crude. I learned of Union Carbon and Carbide's marriage with P. I.'s aggressive National Power to produce scarce fertilizer; of Philippine Corn Products' glucose plant, first in the islands.

And I learned of oil, black gold whose lure has a U. S. company and a local consortium racing feverishly for a strike. Oil is there— an extension of the rich Indies fields. Caltex' new Batangas refinery, and those planned by Shell and Stanvac, all are betting on a strike. The islands are doing fine now—add oil, and they're home in a breeze.

The new republic, nurtured in democracy and freely given independence, is America's showcase in Asia. We glow from her successes and suffer with her failures. How are *we* doing?

U. S. Senator Ellender's report on our worldwide-assistance programs—"some good, some bad, some . . . ridiculous"— said enthusiastically that the program in the Philippines is "very impressive . . . actually, very little money is being spent by us on such programs. We start them, create interest, and the rest . . . is carried on by the people through mutual help." He proudly cited our proposal to close the Iloilo information office, and the Filipinos' offer of financial help to keep it open!

The postwar Hukbalahap rebellion, spawned among tenants sucked dry by absentee landlords, and fanned by the communists, nearly sank the country. Magsaysay saw that land oppression was keeping the movement alive, so he started a resettlement that has given homesteads to 20,000 and, at the time of his death, was pushing roads through lush Mindanao to open up farms for 200,000 more. The usury and antiquated markets that plagued the poor are being ended by ACCFA, government cooperative that since 1954 has set up rural marketing centers and brought the small farmer cheap credit. A $3,000,000 pilot cotton plantation in Mindanao provides its 100 proprietors with all implements and seed—even airplane dusting. This is suggestive of Russia's collective farms, with the vital difference that government and private enterprise are partners. At present 150,000 spindles are taking Indian cotton and local growers want a slice of this lucrative market.

Eight million Filipinos live off the coconut industry. Copra is the No. 1 dollar earner, and Philippine copra has been the worst in the world. Ildefonso Galang owns six hectares (about 15 acres) of Cotabato coastland, and his four-year-old trees (with his garden and a few pigs) bring him a scant $250 a year—from the nation's richest industry. Hence the Coconut Administration's stern ruling that after April 1955 no substandard copra could be exported, for only thus could they shock their improvement program down Ildefonso's throat. Field teams drummed the rules for quality copra production. Fifty coconut companies were born, buying fiber for wallboard, shell for creosote, water for vinegar—by-products which will more than double Ildefonso's take.

Ramie is coming back strong. The world's newest natural textile, it is also the oldest—mummies were shrouded in this forgotten cloth.

Ambuklao, in northern Luzon, is the biggest rock-filled dam in the world

Beside having seven times the strength of silk and growing stronger when wet, this prolific nettle gives six harvests a year. A $3,500,000 all-Filipino corporation has been set up to exploit the "golden weed."

"Go west, young man—and plant coffee!" say experts to erstwhile Filipino pioneers. Coffee loves rich soil and proper elevation, both present in Tagaytay and Mindanao. Standard Brands is making quality Chase and Sanborn from the local bean. Coffee can be a mainstay of the future economy.

Vicente Araneta's new invention of the Arawheel gives tractors floating power in mud fields and permits mechanized tillage of rice paddies. Ford of England, with long tractor experience in India, Ceylon and other rice lands, says it "exceeds the greatest expectations of tractor designers." With slow carabao (water-buffalo) tillage $133 per hectare, and Arawheel tillage only $6.40, Vicente Araneta is the Eli Whitney of riceland.

Bacalod City, proud capital of the sugar belt, burned to the ground not long ago, but within five months this boom town of the south rose from its ashes, finer than ever. Sugar built this wealthy region, and the sugar barons of Negros Occidental are mighty powers in the land. But sugar is an old industry, and reactionary practices and growing U. S. quota restrictions demand that the young dons roll up the fine sleeves of their barong tagalogs if they would weather the rocky years ahead.

Plywood production has grown over 200 times since the war, and its quality can compete in world markets. Gaudencio Manalac, a Davao frontiersman, started three years ago. Today he exports two million board feet a month, logging on a 50-year cycle so his forests will have perpetual yield. The nation's $25,000,000,000 timber wealth is efficiently protected by a smart forest-management plan that enforces a selective-yield logging.

The national highway from La Union to Ilocos Norte is Tobacco Road, and the boom is on. Teodorico Baduria now puts in Virginia Leaf after his rice harvest and makes eight times the amount that rice used to bring him. Frugal Ilocanos aren't buying flashy cars, but put their money in enduring land. Since 1952, tobacco output has swelled from 100,000 to 60,000,000 pounds. The well-run Tobacco Administration is erecting hundreds of the flue-curing barns that small farmers can't afford, plus Agoo's $2,000,000 cooperative redrying plant whose super redryers are the world's only pair except for similar twins in the U. S. Every eight-hour shift this giant can spew out a lusty 90,000 pounds!

The farm boom was sparked by an energetic government dedicated to free enterprise, and steered by the fiscal wizardry of Governor Miguel Cuaderno of the Central Bank. David Grove, Bank of America's chief economist, lauded Cuaderno's "clear vision and technical virtuosity" and flatly stated that "wherever experts gather to discuss . . . economic development he is regarded as a man with few peers." Last fall Cuaderno became Asia's first chairman of both the International Monetary Fund and the International Bank for Reconstruction and Development.

Oil is the open sesame of Philippine prosperity. Lady Tumauini Number One went off strata at 10,000 feet in Isabela.

A hundred miles from Tumauini, Stanvac's Faire Number One is probing the wild Cagayan Valley, where the women roll their own footlong stogies that take three days to smoke. Eleven other companies are exploring, and the Bureau of Mines tells excitedly of 27 seepages in 14 provinces where oil oozes into black pools on the surface. A 50-million-barrel strike would end controls and catalyze myriad new industries hungry for foreign exchange. The keen eyes of many a Philippine financier are fixed on those slender holes that lance Luzon's northern hills.

Hidden in the craggy Philippine hills is the wealth of the Indies. Once, gold from Benguet's mountain mines was king, but in 10 years base metals have swelled 130 times. The most-wanted metal in the U. S. today is said to be nickel. The U. S. has found 550 million tons of nickel-bearing laterite in the P.I.—world's fifth largest source. Surigao's rich billion-ton iron deposit is one of the largest in the world. Atlas Consolidated's 10,000-ton daily copper operation is largest in the Far East, with Lepanto close behind. Palawan Quicksilver, incorporated in late 1954, boomed swiftly to the big board. Vice Commander Carlos Albert of the Navy, who tramped lots of dry land as Roxa's wartime guerilla contact, told me you can ladle the mercury right off the ground! And most pulse-quickening of all is the news of uranium in Camarines Norte!

Japan's steel plants need seven million tons of ore a year. She gets 1.5 million from the Philippines, and fully seven missions have come to the P.I. lately trying to double this figure. Filipinos watch with mixed emotions, looking to the day when their own integrated steel industry can feed the factories of Asia.

The Philippines may be the land of Moro outlaws, of rice terraces which were old when Christ was born, of storied Zamboanga where the monkeys have no tails. But she is a modern sovereign power, too, impatient for her rich land to fulfill its destiny athwart the many trade lanes of the East.

The Little Giant of Southeast Asia is on the march!

From its lofty height, the blimp's radar can scan the skies for miles around

THE BLIMP WON'T

Relatively unheralded since the days of the Hindenburg, the blimp is still around and now is finding new uses in our early-warning defense system

By Walter E. Burton

It looks as if the airship, which has been regarded by some persons as the problem child of the Air Age, is going to survive the newer Electron-Missile-Atom Age. In fact, there are many who believe that it is just now reaching its greatest potential as a military device—that conceivably a lone blimp on a dull patrol mission over a stormy sea could save America from surprise attack.

The airship of today—there are dozens of them in use—is, in numerous ways, vastly different from those in the public eye a generation and more ago when lighter-than-air history then being written by the airships *Akron*, *Macon*, *Graf Zeppelin* and *Hindenburg* was often tinged with tragedy.

So far as is known on the footlight side of the Iron Curtain, there are only two places in the world where airships are being produced.

The bump on top of this ZPG-3W airship houses the height-finder antenna

STAY MOORED

The principal builder is Goodyear Aircraft Corporation's plant in Akron, Ohio. Recently two blimps for commercial purposes were reported under construction at Friedrichshafen, Germany.

There are a number of bases from which blimps are flying, for the nonrigid airship is a part of the defense ring that watches for hostile actions. Such lighter-than-air watchdogs are operated by the United States Navy. In addition, Goodyear still uses a blimp or two for commercial flying—advertising, aerial photography, passenger carrying and sometimes police work. There are no rigid, or true Zeppelin-type, airships in use.

Last July the ZPG-3W, first of a new and larger class of nonrigid airships for airborne early-warning picket patrol, made its maiden flight in Akron. The largest nonrigid airship ever built, the ZPG-3W is about 50 percent larger than the ZPG-2.

The new airships being built at Akron have to be large, for they will carry the heaviest array of radar equipment ever sent into the skies to watch for possible invaders. Each ship will hold 1.5 million cubic feet of helium, 50 percent more than the capacity of the biggest blimp that had previously been in service; and it will be close to two city blocks long.

The modern nonrigid airship is as different from its ancestors of

Marking flares are part of the early-warning equipment

25 to 30 years ago as is the modern automobile in comparison with cars of that period. Here are some of the airship's advances, as outlined by Goodyear Aircraft officials:

The Bag, or Envelope. Research has been going on constantly in an effort to improve the rubberized fabric used for confining the gas that gives the airship nearly all its lift (some aerodynamic lift is produced by rapid movement of the bag through the air). For a while after the last World War, rubberized three-ply cotton was used, then was replaced by less heavy two-ply cotton. Now cotton has given way to synthetic fabrics. A rubberized Dacron envelope (two-ply) weighs, per unit area, only about 60 percent as much as two-ply cotton. For some reason not yet fully understood, the Dacron bag material has a remarkable ability to hold helium—so much so that, in a year's time, helium needed to replace that lost by diffusion and other causes equals no more than a single filling of the bag. The Dacron bag material is said to be so strong mechanically that an inch-wide strip can support two overweight men.

The Car. In earlier days, a blimp car was a fabric-covered tubular-steel affair. Now it is of airplane-type construction, made largely of a "sandwich" material consisting of two thicknesses of 0.008-inch sheet aluminum having between them ¼ inch of either balsa wood or aluminum honeycomb. The cabin of a ship such as a ZPG-2 has two decks. The lower one is the work level, and contains control equipment and electronic and other military gear. The upper level is occupied by living quarters. To reduce the boredom of long flights, designers have tried to provide most of the comforts of home—food freezer, well equipped galley, a wardroom for cards and other relaxation. Living compartments are finished in gay colors.

Power Plants. The two engines are of latest-design reciprocating type, are gasoline-driven and so mounted that they can be serviced and repaired in flight. They drive variable-pitch propellers that can be instantly feathered or reversed. The pilot of today's airship no longer has to worry about prop control: He sets his engines for a certain speed, say 1600 revolutions per minute; then automatic controls alter the propeller pitch so that the engine speed remains constant no matter what the ship's speed requirements.

Likewise, other ship controls have been given the push-button treatment. The modern blimp has "power steering," for servomechanisms move the tail-control surfaces: No longer does the pilot have to spin an elevator-control wheel or tug to move stubborn cables. Nor does he have to be constantly concerned with pressure inside the helium bag. He merely sets a dial for the pressure desired, such as two inches of water. A newly developed device then automatically maintains this pressure within a tolerance of .050 inch of water. Because blimp pilots often are also airplane pilots, standard airplane controls and instruments are used wherever possible, and are grouped as on airplanes.

Maintenance. An airship is a "long endurance" vehicle, and so it must be possible to make equipment repairs in flight. To facilitate this, electronic units are on long cables so they can be pulled out on the cabin floor for servicing. Or they can be disconnected and taken to a

Last year a blimp set a record by flying 11 days nonstop, without refueling

repair bench for test and overhaul. In the same way, all other equipment that may require inflight servicing is made easy to reach.

Ground Crews. In earlier days, ground crews of 30 or more nimble men might be needed to handle a small airship in landing or taking off. Today, mobile mooring masts and heavy but extremely mobile ground-handling tractors, operated by a few men, do the job more efficiently. Ships can remain moored to their masts in all sorts of weather, swinging in the wind like huge weathervanes. They can land and take off at almost any airfield.

Equipment. Just about the biggest difference between the newest naval airships and those of a generation and a half ago is in the stuff they carry. An early-warning blimp is jammed with radar and other electronic gear. That is why the bag capacity has had to be increased to the million-and-a-half point; the extra lift is needed for extra gear. In the latest design, a gigantic radar-search antenna revolves inside the airship's bag, thus making the bag a radome. This has necessitated the use of plastic instead of aluminum for the ship's nose cone and adjacent bracing—to minimize reflection of the radar impulses. The only metal at the nose is the "flowerpot" by which the ship is moored.

The big antenna suspended inside the ship's envelope is said to enable the radar to achieve better performance, including greater range, than any other type of airborne installation. Besides, "sea clutter" caused by reflection of radar impulses from nearby waves is lessened. Compared with a plane, an airship is considered a gentle sort of vehicle. It moves smoothly, experiences few sudden bumps or jerks; and because everything is suspended from a gas-filled fabric-and-rubber bubble, the gear is in a naturally cushioned mounting. This reduces wear and tear on delicate electronic equipment, permits more accurate readings and means less time and energy lost in maintenance.

Commercial Uses. The idea of using airships for commercial purposes, such as carrying pay loads, advertising, aerial photography, exploring and police work, is far from being dead. Almost daily, Goodyear Aircraft people receive inquiries from persons who think an airship would be ideal for certain jobs. What generally stops them is the little matter of money. Airships require capital for building and operating commercially. By comparison, in such military work as antisubmarine patrolling and early-warning watching, they are said to be less expensive than comparable heavier-than-air units. Even if this were not true, the airship still would be considered valuable in defense work, for it is maintained that, on the basis of records of two World Wars, nothing has been found superior to the airship for antisubmarine patrolling, especially in connection with convoys.

In this day of many kinds of missiles, the airship is considered to be virtually no more vulnerable than the airplane. That is, in action involving missiles of tremendous destructive power, it would not matter much whether an aircraft in missile range were traveling with the speed and maneuverability of a plane or with the relative leisure of an airship.

Thus with respect to technical developments, the airship has not been standing still. And because of its new-found ability to function as a long-range flying radar station, plus its war-proved knack of finding and scaring off or sinking submarines, it seems likely that it will be around for some time to come.

Henri and Jacques in southern Chile with Osborno volcano in the background

Across Four Continents on Two Cylinders

By Jacques Cornet as told to Richard F. Dempewolff

Sputtering noisily, our battle-scarred, heroic beetle of a Citroen wheezed and shuddered over the cobbled square of Notre Dame de Paris and ground to a halt at the curb. A welcoming committee of one excited, gesticulating gendarme promptly greeted us with a ticket for parking in a restricted zone. But who cared? This was home—home after 367 days and 32,292 rugged miles of driving, the likes of which would put a bulldozer to the supreme test.

It was impossible now to believe. Our little 1100-lb., 9-horsepower vehicle, popping along on two cylinders, had teetered on dizzy mountain burro trails that had never seen a tire. Stripped to little more than chassis and body frame, it had jounced over rock outcrops to cross a roadless Andean peak 17,000 feet in the Bolivian sky. It had put-putted faithfully across the trackless, desolate wastes of Patagonia to the southernmost tip of the Americas. Tired engine throbbing with heat, it had carried us 1000 miles over the burning Sahara Desert, where a compass showed the route. In fact, thinking back, it seems a remarkable number of those 32,292 miles were roadless. Life was a nightmare of plunging through swamps and creek beds, swishing through sand on beaches at low tide to circumvent impassable mountains, bounding cross-country with only the stars for road signs—and heaven knew what obstacles ahead.

Naturally, all this was something more than just a carefree summer motor tour. For four years, my friend Henri Lochon had nursed a burning desire to drive a car down the Pan American Highway—from Mexico clear to Tierra del Fuego, last point of land at the foot of South America. He talked about it ceaselessly on the holiday motor trips we took around Europe—to the Austrian Alps for skiing, Cannes for spear fishing, to Italy, Spain and Corsica just for sight-seeing. Motoring was a hobby we enjoyed and shared together at every opportunity. I agreed that South America was a fine idea, but my desire was to tour North America.

"Why not do both?" Henri said one day. "Pool our money, buy a new car and plan a year's expedition across all of the Americas. We

Crossing Chile's Atacama Desert makes one think he is driving on the moon

could then make a tour that probably no car has ever covered."

The next months were a maelstrom of planning and preparation, much of it undertaken by Henri, since this was his "baby." Because of its small size, light weight, and the fact it can be easily dismantled to go almost anywhere, the Citroen seemed like a good car for our journey. It has a simple two-cylinder air-cooled engine and a rugged four-speed transmission. It holds four passengers. With Henri and me in front, the entire rear could be used for our gear, food, and reserve water and fuel. Another unique feature is that the doors and side panels of this little car are removable simply by slipping them out of slots. For driving through mud, or up precipitous slopes, such a reduction in weight can mean the difference between going someplace or turning around in defeat. This feature was to save our expedition many times before we were through. The car was standard except for one modification in the suspension system. The wheels were mounted on movable arms, tied together by a system of spring rods similar to torsion bars. With the rear of the car weighted, rocking motion was thus controlled, resulting in a firm, flat ride and plenty of clearance.

Left, the only gas station for 1000 miles in Patagonia; right, "paving" a road

Sometimes mulepower was better than horsepower for pulling car out of mud

At 3 p.m. on May 8, 1953, our compact expedition roared bravely out of the plaza in front of Notre Dame, while dozens of friends cheered and waved us off. It was a year and two days before we saw them again. In no time, we were weaving through jumbled traffic in the waterfront streets of Le Havre. We watched from the pier as a deck crane lifted our car in a sling and lowered her through a yawning hatch into the hold of the British ship *Scythia.* We didn't see it again until the *Scythia* sailed up the St. Lawrence River and deposited us at Quebec. From that ancient walled city, on May 20, our great adventure on wheels really began.

The first leg, on good Canadian and United States roads, whizzed by without mishap. Our two-cylinder bug "sang" up the St. Lawrence valley, through Montreal, Niagara Falls, New York and Washington. Along the way we began to hear rumors that we might not have clear sailing through Central and South America. And, at Pan American Union headquarters in Washington, the rumors were confirmed.

"The Pan American highway does not link the Americas," the man said.

Good blacktop highway spears through Mexico, we learned—but at the Guatemalan border the road would peter out to muddy cart ruts, cattle trails and a jagged mountain wilderness for an impassable 25 miles. After that, we might make it along poorly graded one-way paths hanging on mountainsides to Guatemala City, and over fair roads in El Salvador. But in Costa Rica a good highway that soars to a pass 11,000 feet high, from which one would see both oceans, suddenly dead-ends against a mountain and doesn't pick up again until 150 miles later in Panama.

"Worst of all," said our informer, "is a 250-mile gap in the steaming tropical rain forest of Darien, south of Panama, where hostile Indians inhabit jungles and swamps that make the Everglades look like a duck marsh. This part has never even been surveyed for roadway. In southern

The Citroen was not designed to be amphibious, but fortunately for us it was

Ecuador another nonexistent section separates Riobamba and Macara, and your car will have to be carried by plane or train."

What about all those rugged fellows we'd heard about who drove jeeps and "house trucks" from Alaska to Argentina and wrote articles? Our friend grinned. "No one has driven from Alaska to Argentina—or will in our lifetime, probably."

With this gruesome news, we headed for the West Coast via Detroit, Chicago and Salt Lake City, determined to try our luck anyway.

Through San Francisco, Los Angeles and El Paso we purred along as planned. The sunlit landscapes of Mexico whirled past in a panoramic kaleidoscope of towering mountains and fields, huts and mansions. Colorful Indians and drab peasants trudged the roadside, leading dejected little burros buried under prodigious loads. We ducked and dodged madcap Mexico City taxi drivers whose least concern is another car or a pedestrian. Still we zoomed southward with a problem— through Puebla, Mitla and Oaxaca, where we stopped long enough to see the magnificent Zapotec temples that had been destroyed by the Spanish conquistadores, and to tighten up our steed, check her tires, fuel and engine performance for what lay ahead.

At Tehuantepec we ran out of hard-surface highway, and never saw any again until Oran, 20,000 miles later.

Now the fun began. Guatemalan border mountains loomed ahead. The road narrowed to a rutted, rocky ox path that rapidly dwindled to a foot trail through towering forests. A normal car could never have squeezed between the trunks of virgin jungle giants that crowded our Citroen. The first river was easily forded. Then came another—deeper. We pushed the Citroen across. Then another and another. Jungle closed in until we had to alternate walking in front of the car with a machete to clear a path, signaling the way to the driver. Advancing a few feet at a time we came to the edge of a rushing stream, and drove

In emergencies we improvised. Here we replace a broken jack with stones

confidently into it. Almost instantly, the wet motor died. For hours we battled with rope, tackle and jacks, inching our dismantled car to the opposite shore while the glittering eyes of ugly five-foot iguanas peered at us from the foliage. Once across, lianas tangled around us. The car sank in soft earth. No amount of chopping or hauling would free it. Steaming heat descended like a fog, and the mosquitoes went to work on us. We were stuck. This was it. Henri threw up his hands. "Back to the Mexican National Railroad," he announced. "We aren't the first."

That night was spent in the jungle. Without emergency food and equipment it might have been worse. Next day, we stripped the car and pulled it by hand line some 10 miles to the tracks. Then another trip to pack in the rest of our gear. We waved down the first freight and piled aboard for the half-day train ride around the mountains into Guatemala.

Except for incredible 45-degree slopes that worked our little two-cylinder engine to fiery heat, requiring many cooling-off stops, the mountainous road to Guatemala City from the railhead was fairly good. It curled through spectacular canyons, past lush coffee plantations, Mayan ruins and the fabulous palace of Antigua from where Spaniards once ruled all of Central America. After ignition and tire repairs at Guatemala City, we headed south again, good as new. And for hundreds of miles through El Salvador and Nicaragua, everything was great. We began to scoff at the dark tales we'd heard.

Then we saw the terrifying, jagged peaks that separate Nicaragua from Costa Rica. What's more, the rainy season was in full swing. As we progressed, the road became a sewer of mud—three feet deep in spots. We bogged down a dozen times, finally unloaded, jacked up the Citroen and put on chains while a knot of wet, bedraggled Indians

Here we pause for an oil and water break en route on the Atacama Desert

gathered to watch and shake their heads. Not a man, they told us, had been down this road in four months. We must be crazy. For a while the chains helped. Then, thigh-deep in muck, we pushed, hauled and rocked from one mudhole to the next, advancing a few feet at a time. Wheels churned against nothing, the engine overheated, the heat was sickening. Finally, the little car thumped into a huge hole and gave up. It took six mules and as many drivers to pull us out of there—and we decided to take to the sea. We thumped and ground our way to the coast where we boarded a ship for the Panamanian border. From there to Panama City, the road was good. And when we learned on arrival that a French ship was about to depart for Buenaventura, Colombia, we gave up all thought of attempting the Darien jungle and just drove aboard.

After the wilderness, the mosaic pavements of Rio de Janeiro looked wonderful

In Bolivia, our Citroen made a record-breaking climb of 17,000 feet

Once cleared by customs, we lost no time getting out of Buena-ventura. Though pitted and washed out, the road was passable. But the creaking, rotten wooden bridges gave us many a qualm. Outside Cali, on the way to Bogota at night, one of these ancient contraptions finally did come apart under us. With a thundering crash the floor gave way and we crashed nose-first into the river bank, exploding both front tires, denting the wheels and snapping the axle. We had barely hauled the car up to the roadside when we heard shots and galloping horses from a nearby hill. Someone had heard us. We'd been warned not to travel at night. Guerillas lurking in these hills shot at anyone. Though famed for their remarkable inaccuracy with guns, stray shots had been known to graze people now and then. We doused the lights and waited. The first horseman shot past us, thundered right through the hole in the bridge, bashed himself against the far embank-ment and lay groaning. Those following reined in just in time to avoid the same fate, and rushed to his assistance with much chattering. The confusion played into our hands. Henri flipped the ignition, hit the starter and the faithful little car revved up in fine shape. Flat tires, bent wheels, broken axle and all, she went shuddering down the road

Nothing ever looked as good as Paris did when we returned to France

at a great clip. Those horsemen never knew what took off from there.

We limped into Bogota next morning and cabled a friend in Paris to send new axle, tires and parts by air. They arrived in two days. We waited six more while the damage was repaired by an Indian "mechanic" who could not understand us, nor we him. This may be why he installed the axle upside down—who knows? The error came to light 5000 miles later when, grinding over a pass in the Chilean Andes, the upside-down axle, unable to stand the unusual stress imposed on it, snapped in two and left our front wheels knock-kneed.

Until that happened, there were other things to prevent lethargy. The Citroen bounded unhappily along the poorly graded mountain roads through Ecuador—frequently bottoming out on rocks jutting from the high-crowned, deeply rutted trails. By the time we hit the interminable straightaway to Lima, on the Peruvian coast, seven breaks in the chassis were held together precariously with baling wire. Every place we stopped, curious natives gathered to stare at the muddy, wobbly little car and its haggard occupants. Tropical showers drowned us one moment, and white-hot sun baked us dry the next as we chugged through endless banana groves and oil fields.

At Lima, we welded broken parts, rebuilt our car and enjoyed the sights. By the time we finished, the Citroen was in such good shape we decided to alter course, head inland to the Bolivian Andes, and try for an altitude record. The grueling ascent through Nazca, Cuzo and Puno to the 14,000-foot heights of La Paz and Lake Titicaca, was only a beginning. Here, llamas grazed and people moved slowly in the rarefied air. Strength left our legs, temples throbbed, and breath came in quick gasps with the least exertion. Even the Citroen throbbed. At La Paz we removed the car's side panels and doors, stripped her to nothing but engine and frame and chugged up the barren, roadless slopes of a 17,777-foot peak—an all-time high for Citroen.

From there, it was all downhill. For ten days we clattered around hairpin curves and down hair-raising mountain trails to the Chilean coast. At Iquique, we stocked supplies of food and water for the 1750 miles of desert between us and Santiago. Stopping only to eat, we drove day and night across the wind-whipped sands in an immensity of space. By now, our tires that had been new in Colombia, were going flat at a rate of four times a day. After recuperating at Santiago for two weeks, we pressed southward to Puerto Montt, where roads and beaches gave way to precipitous mountain slopes plunging vertically into the sea.

Henri, myself and the Citroen went aboard one Captain Francisco's little 100-ton schooner plying among the islands. We were put ashore several hundred miles down the coast at Puerto Aysen, a fishing town of white houses, board sidewalks and sailors, reminiscent of a hundred Scandinavian ports. From here, the rock-bound coasts rose to the barren steppes of Patagonia. We'd heard about the terrible winds, sweeping up from the South Polar seas, that constantly batter this roadless land of rocky desolation. But we had no idea, as we set out toward our goal of Tierra del Fuego, how badly it would buffet us. Gales of 60 to 90 miles per hour lashed us in fury the entire distance. Our hands and faces stung from pebbles—up to the size of marbles— whipped into the air and driven before the blast. We drove largely by compass, since the lashing wind erased all but the faintest trace of trails. Except for an occasional refugee rancher, the only signs of life were a few ostriches, guanacos and scuttling rabbits. Life was a succession of flat tires.

By Christmas, we had made the rugged 1000 miles to Punta Arenas on the Strait of Magellan. We were bedraggled and hungry. Here, where the sunlight lasted 20 hours a day, we used the meager facilities of the isolated village to repair the Citroen and ready ourselves for the dash to the southernmost civilized town on the western continents— Ushuaia, on the southern coast of Tierra del Fuego. We were warned we'd never make it. There was no road. Steep rocky cliffs plunged to beaches completely inundated at high tide, and a mountain range blocked the last 10 miles. But it was worth a try.

Chilean marines agreed to sail us across the strait in a landing barge. So, at three o'clock one morning, to more head-shaking and dire predictions, we sailed south. Six hours later, our marine friends wished us well and left us on the beach at Marantiales. Following advice, we banged and bumped along the shore of a small river named Rio Grande and found shelter that night in an isolated ranch owned by a refugee Belgian who informed us there was no road at all from here. We would have to take the beach at low tide. Leaving at 8 a.m. would give us four hours to go 30 miles—plenty of time if the tires held us. If not? We might have to climb the cliffs and walk home.

Luck was with us. The tires held and by noon we were back on a so-called road, off the beach. But after 50 miles the road dwindled away to nothing but limitless waste—a land of birds, millions of them, so fearless they had to be shooed from the path with sticks. Then, a rushing river blocked the way and, halfway across, the car stuck. Baggage floated down the current as we struggled for four hours, dismantling the car panels and doors so we could pull it out. More hours were lost starting it again. Rain and snow began to pelt us, and the trail became a mire that soon froze. A dozen times we pried the car out of holes and ditches into which it skidded. Chains were little help. Our feet and hands were blue with cold, but still we inched ahead through country no car had ever traveled. In three hours we made two miles on a donkey trail leading up through the last mountain range. Suddenly, we found ourselves wedged between the cliff wall and a 500-foot precipice. We could go no further. The ledge ahead was narrower than the car. In that precarious place we had to turn the car around and find refuge before nightfall at 11 p.m.— three hours off. It was too dangerous to back down. Lifting, heaving and coaxing, we almost made it—then a back wheel slipped over the edge and hung, spinning, in space. Digging one foot in a crevice of the cliff wall, and using a stout sapling for a lever, Henri pried mightily against the dangling wheel while I heaved and tugged at the car. A slight gust now would have sent the teetering vehicle plunging over the edge. Inch by inch it came around. At last, numb and weary, we climbed aboard and banged down the trail to a settler's hut we had passed on the way up.

The slow return back across the strait in the landing barge, up across wind-swept Patagonia, then off to the east coast for Buenos Aires, Sao Paulo and Rio, was anticlimactic. Our second set of tires peeled off in ribbons on the desolate steppes, and we drove 2000 miles into Buenos Aires on the rims, clanking along over rocks like a rolling garbage can full of loose rivets.

The banquets, parties and hospitality of the people who welcomed us in the glamour cities of Argentina and Brazil quickly erased the grim memories of our ordeal. And, with the Citroen once more welded back in one piece, equipped with a new set of wheels and washed, things looked brighter. So bright that in Rio we made the foolhardy decision to sail for Dakar, instead of France as originally planned, and travel back across the Sahara Desert to set another record. We would coast home via the Senegal, Sudan, Bamako on the Niger River, around the mountains to Oran, down to Casablanca, up to Rabat and Tangiers. Then, across Gibraltar, up through Spain—and Paris!

The wonder is we ever made it. We had overestimated the ability of our stout little vehicle—and ourselves. Had the car been new, we might have had no trouble—but with 25,000 miles of hideous punishment under its hood, we were asking too much. The Sahara is a cruel desert.

A few hundred miles out of Dakar, on the burning sands, our troubles began. The new tires overheated and exploded continually. The battery went dead, and we stuck pitifully time and time again in the endless horizons of loose, drifted sand. Our meager stock of drinking water was quickly consumed, as we worked, perspiring in the 120-degree heat to push the car out of sand traps. Two hundred miles from anywhere, our water was gone. For two days we went without any as we struggled to move the car a few miserable miles over the wastes. Not a living soul did we pass. Our lips blistered and tongues began to swell. That night as we lay down to sleep in the cool side of a dune, neither of us spoke. We knew another day would spell the end.

Morning brought no cheer until, suddenly, Henri gave a hoarse croak and pointed toward the horizon. There, creeping across the dunes against the sky was a camel caravan. headed our way! They were Taureg traders. No sight in the world could have been more beautiful. The brackish water from their sour goatskin sacks tasted like a cool, crystal mountain spring to our parched mouths. These Samaritans of the desert fed us, rested us and then, with one young camel hitched to the front of the Citroen, we were towed ingloriously for 20 miles to an oasis. Making emergency repairs, we managed to limp on into Bamako where the car was serviced and refitted with new tires. The remainder of the journey to Oran was a nightmare of digging ourselves out of sand pits, minor breakdowns, and waiting in the scorching sun for trucks to come and tow us out of trouble. Then came Oran and the nightmares were gone. Once again we drove on flat, hardtop roads, purring along as though nothing in the world had ever stopped us.

And so we proceeded back to Paris at a tourist's amble, to the Plaza in front of Notre Dame. Under our belts was a great adventure and an assortment of outstanding records. Would we do it again? I can't speak for Henri, but I know that, for myself, I am going to be content to settle down to the pursuit of my new profession—photography. Whether or not it will take me to the corners of the world again, who knows?

TALKING WITH FANGIO

about the 1958 Indianapolis 500 and European Grand Prix racing. It was during this interview with PM Editor Art Railton that Fangio announced his retirement

Question: Mr. Fangio, would you like to explain, for the record, why you did not race at Indianapolis?

Fangio: I would like to have raced there, but I must have a good car and the training necessary to drive a good race, to be able to compete with the best drivers there. I must have a chance to win, at least.

Q: Then there were two reasons: One, the lack of sufficient training time on the track and two, the Dayton car was not fast enough. Is that right?

Fangio: Yes. Actually, it was only after I tested the car that I found out it did not have a very good background. I had to drive it on the track to find out.

Giambertone: We didn't go to Indianapolis to race. We only went there to test the Dayton car to see if we would race.

Fangio: With that car I didn't have a chance.

Q: How old is the Dayton car?

Giambertone: This is its third year. It ran in 1956, in 1957 and again in 1958. It's an old car. All last year it was stored in a wooden shack.

Fangio: They told me they would change the engine and perhaps the car would go faster. Maybe yes, maybe no. They didn't know because they never tested the engine on the bench. They were going to assemble it and install it in the car. But it was too late to change engines.

Q: How fast did you drive the car?

Fangio: I drove it 142 miles per hour while the other cars on the track were making 146 and 147. It didn't have a chance.

Q: Did you have enough training time?

Fangio: I was in Indianapolis 15 days but I only had two days of training.

Giambertone: We arrived on May 4th. He made 12 laps in the morning, 14 in the afternoon. The car wasn't doing too well. It rained on the 5th and 6th. On the 7th he made eight laps and the car stopped. Something was wrong with the carburetor. Later he went about 30 laps before taking his driver's test. On May 10th it ran beautifully in the test. He made 10 laps at 115 miles per hour, 10 at 120, 10 at 125 and 10 at 130. The race officials were enthused about the precision of Fangio's driving during his test.

Q: Do you think, Mr. Fangio, that the rules are unfair to new drivers?

Fangio: No, they are fair. The driver's test they give is very well done. I have no criticism of the test or the procedures. Everything is very well organized. They take more precautions at Indianapolis than anywhere I have ever driven. It is the safest of all tracks both for the driver and the public. There are 33 cars in a small circuit and they have to make the best possible selection of cars and drivers. And they do.

Q: How do you like the Indianapolis track itself?

Fangio: It is very good for speed.

Q: What is the hardest thing to learn about driving at Indianapolis?

Fangio: The confidence you must have in your car to go into the curves fast.

Q: Is this something psychological?

Fangio: Not psychological, but mathematical. Once you learn, it is like running on a rail. After that, it's easy.

Q: Does the Indianapolis race require more endurance for the driver than a Grand Prix race?

Fangio won the 1957 Cuban race in this Maserati. During the 1958 race the "Old Man" was kidnapped by Castro's revolutionists and didn't get to race

Fangio: I don't know, but 200 laps at Indianapolis must be very hard on a driver.

Q: Would the closed circuit at Indianapolis be monotonous to the driver?

Fangio: I've never raced at Indianapolis, but I don't think it would be monotonous for the driver. It might be monotonous for the public, but not for the driver.

Q: Do you think any European car could win at Indianapolis?

Fangio: No. For Indianapolis you need a specially made car.

Giambertone: We are very grateful to Crawford, Bryan and other drivers who gave advice to Fangio. They taught Fangio how to go around corners. He was going around them like they do in Europe, accelerating. Here it's different. If you accelerate while going around a corner you go off the track. You can't race here the way they do in Europe. I doubt if a European could win this race even with the best car. The Indianapolis driver starts racing on a dirt track and learns to drive around curves without accelerating. At Indianapolis, Fangio, in spite of being the world's champion, had to learn all over again.

Fangio: These Indianapolis drivers start on small dirt race tracks. Later they go to bigger races and finally to Indianapolis. The Indianapolis race driver is highly specialized.

Q: Will any Europeans come to Indianapolis and race?

Fangio: I doubt it. But anyone who does come will have to come with plenty of time to learn.

Giambertone: Let me explain it this way: Fangio is like a general practitioner who treats general ailments of the body. He does everything. You wouldn't go to him if you had a heart ailment, you'd go to a heart specialist. These Indianapolis drivers are "heart specialists" in racing. If they had to drive in Europe's Grand Prix, they wouldn't be able to do anything.

Q: Did you have a language problem because you don't speak English?

Champion Fangio won the 1957 Sebring 12-hour race in this 4.5 Maserati

Giambertone: No. We had a friend with us who speaks English well. And there is something else: International racers have their own special language. They understand each other with their eyes.

Q: Would you like to come back to Indianapolis and race with a good car next year?

Fangio: From now to next year is a lot of time, but I would like to come back. But if I don't have a chance to win a race, I shouldn't be in it.

Q: Did the Dayton group invite you to race in its car?

Fangio: Of course. They told me the car had 420 horsepower, that it was the best car available there. So I came over to try out the car with no strings attached. I told them that if what they told me was true, I would race. I don't want the best car in the race, but I do want one that will at least give me an even chance.

Q: What is the difference between an Indianapolis car and a Grand Prix car?

Fangio: Well, to begin with, the Indianapolis car has no gearshift. It isn't necessary. And the brakes are almost unnecessary. They are used very little. European cars have as many as five gears. There are a lot of curves to go around. The cars have to be able to go this way and that way, to the right, to the left. At Indianapolis it is all to the left.

Q: What about the engines?

Fangio: The Meyer and Drake is good for Indianapolis but it wouldn't be very good in Europe. First of all, the formula in Europe is 2½ liters, this engine is too big. And the European engines have to go through gears so they develop more revolutions. They go up to 8000 and 9000 revolutions per minute. The Indianapolis engines get only up to 6000 or so.

Q: Does anything worthwhile come from auto racing? Is racing worth the risk?

Fangio: I think there are more engineering developments from Grand Prix racing than from Indianapolis. After all, Indianapolis is a round-and-round race. It isn't like normal driving where you stop, turn right and left. Nowhere does the public use a car as it is used in Indianapolis. Once the driver has learned the trick of making the corners it is almost like a straightaway.

Q: Why do you think Americans have more interest in the round-and-round race than the Grand Prix type?

Fangio: I think it is because this way the promoters can charge a fee to everyone who watches the race. It's a matter of business.

Q: What percentage of the victory depends on the car, what percentage on the driver's skill?

Fangio: Seventy-five percent is the car, 25 percent the driver. When you become famous, the companies offer you the best car to drive so it is easier to win because 75 percent is the car.

Q: What type of person makes the best driver?

Fangio: Any type. We are all the same. What is needed is a lot of training and running in many races. Nobody is born knowing how to race, nobody is special.

Q: Of all the cars you have raced, which one did you like the best, which had the best "feel?"

Fangio: The Mercedes I raced in 1954 and 1955.

Q: How important is bravery to a driver?

Fangio: Courage is not the important thing. You have to know how to figure your speed and how to go safely into a curve. I don't think of auto racing as going into a battlefield or challenging death.

Q: There is talk of banning racing here because of the accidents. Do you think races could be made safer?

Fangio: They are taking the necessary precautions, especially at Indianapolis. When the necessary measures are not taken, as in some countries, the public always gathers in the most dangerous spots.

Q: Are you going to race after this year?

Fangio: This is my last year. This year I am only racing to satisfy a few commitments. I am too old. I am semi-retired.

Q: Is there any indication that this country is becoming more interested in Grand Prix racing?

Fangio: Yes. It seems that some promoters are thinking now of having races of the Grand Prix type over here.

Giambertone: We talked with Tony Hulman, the owner of the Indianapolis speedway. He wants to hold a Grand Prix race at the track with Formula One cars involving at least five or six Americans.

Q: Mr. Giambertone, do you think a race like the Indianapolis race would draw a big crowd in Europe?

Giambertone: Very much so. I have been thinking about holding one there.

Q: Who do you think is the best American driver in the Grand Prix circuit?

Giambertone: Phil Hill is the best, next is Harry Schell, then Masten Gregory and Carroll Shelby in that order.

Here is Fangio after passing driver's test at Indianapolis Speedway in 1958

WILL WE DIG ORE WITH ATOM BOMBS?

Recent tests suggest that we may be able to use atomic bombs for peaceful purposes. Here is a report on the underground Rainier shot

It may be possible to rejuvenate old oil fields, open up vast deposits of low grade ores, and create huge underground water reservoirs for arid regions, all with atomic bombs.

That's the opinion of AEC scientists who are studying the results of deep underground atomic blasts that have been touched off at their Nevada test site. One of the explosions, the Rainier shot, was a "tiny" atom bomb only a tenth as powerful as the bomb dropped on Hiroshima, yet it crushed 500,000 tons of rock and broke up an additional 200,000 tons.

The intense heat of the explosion dissipated quite rapidly and yet three months later some of the rock still had a temperature of 190 degrees Fahrenheit, close to the boiling point of water.

The bomb was exploded at the end of a tunnel 900 feet below the surface of a mesa, in porous, water-saturated volcanic tuff. The tunnel was curved somewhat like a spiral so that it would be sealed by the blast, preventing any escape of radiation.

Spectators saw nothing but a ripple in the earth and numerous spurts of dust from dislodged rocks when the bomb was fired. Few of them felt any shock, though a slight tremor was recorded at scattered seismograph stations as far away as Alaska.

To study the effects of the bomb, the Atomic Energy Commission drilled exploratory holes from the surface of the mesa and from a point in the original tunnel. By examining the corings that were brought out by the drills the scientists were able to trace the story of what the explosion had done.

When the bomb went off, its terrific pressure pushed out the walls of the small chamber at the end of the tunnel and created a spherical cavity 110 feet in diameter. The walls of the cavity were fused by the intense heat into a four-inch-thick layer of black, glasslike material.

The surrounding rock for a distance of 75 feet was crushed almost into sand, then squeezed so hard that it became impermeable to water. Farther away, the rock was unchanged, though it "jumped" sufficiently to seal the access tunnel 200 feet from the explosion point. The blast also shattered large amounts of rock in the tunnel as far as 400 feet away.

Almost immediately after the explosion the spherical cavity collapsed. The upper half of the glassy lining fell to the floor, and the unsupported rock above it caved in. Additional rock collapsed from above, then more rock. This continued until a strong rock layer 368 feet above the explosion point was reached. In effect, a "chimney" of loose, unconsolidated material was produced.

Aside from a little radioactive gas in the chimney, virtually all radioactivity was confined to the mass of glass-like liner that lay in the lower portion of the original cavity.

Main purpose of the Rainier shot was to learn whether a nuclear weapon that was tested underground would eliminate the usual radioactive clouds, fallout, and flash and noise of an ordinary test. The experiment was a complete success. No radiation escaped to the atmosphere and there appears little chance that ground water could become contaminated.

In this test the underground rock cooled off quite rapidly because of its high water content. The heat turned the water into steam which then escaped through pores and fissures. In relatively dry rock, temperatures of possibly 1000 degrees might have persisted for months.

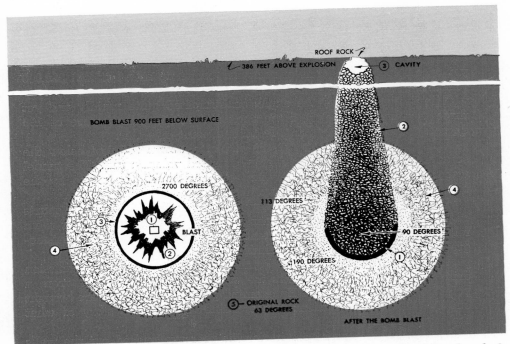

Drawing at left shows how blast in tunnel, 1, made cavity, 2, with walls of fused rock, 3, which trapped radiation. Surrounding rock, 4, was crushed. At right, roof collapsed, leaving bowl, 1, of fused material and 386-foot high tower, 2, of broken rock

Scientists think that a much bigger bomb, exploded in dry rock, would create a great storehouse of heat which could then be tapped and converted into power. Dr. Willard F. Libby of the Atomic Energy Commission says that this may be done. The idea would be to pump water through the hot area, producing superheated steam that would be used to drive an electric generator. Some preliminary research on the idea is being done now.

Another possibility is to use underground atomic blasts to recover more oil from depleted oil fields. Petroleum engineers say that no more than a third of the crude oil in an underground pool is extracted by pumping. Secondary recovery methods produce a little more, but possibly 50 percent remains in the ground. Still more should become available by an underground blast. The pressure created by the explosion would help free the oil trapped in relatively nonporous rock formations, and the heat of the blast would make the oil flow more freely.

The thought of creating underground water reservoirs is based on the expectation that a controlled blast could shatter immense quantities of rock underneath the run-off canyons of mountain ranges in arid areas. Rainwater from mountain storms would then percolate underground and be stored, instead of running off along surface channels and evaporating.

Dr. Libby says that the cost of moving big quantities of earth and rock by atomic explosions is pretty low. He mentions the construction or improvement of harbors as one possible job for atomic bombs. There are still others. The creation of radioactive isotopes on a mass scale is one possibility, new and useful chemicals from nuclear explosions in thick coal seams is another.

As an aid to mining, there have been suggestions that big mineral deposits that are so low grade they can't now be worked at a profit could be profitably mined if broken up by an atomic blast. One buried bomb could shatter a whole mountain of low-grade copper ore, for instance, and the ore would then be ready for transportation to a concentrating mill. It might even be practical to leave the ore where it is and to leach the valuable minerals from it with liquids that would trickle down through the shattered formation.

The AEC has created a special department called Project Plowshare to investigate all such peaceful uses of controlled atomic explosions. The work is centered at the University of California's Radiation Laboratory at Livermore, Calif.

One of the Project Plowshare studies will determine the feasibility of using atomic bombs to dig a harbor on the coast of Alaska. Personnel from the University of California Radiation Laboratory are gathering geological and ocean data, as well as cost figures, in connection with the proposal to blast a deep-water haven for ships between Cape Thompson and Cape Seppings, above the Arctic Circle.

The scientists also will try to learn what effects such an atomic explosion would have upon the people and the fish and wildlife of the area.

The AEC has pointed out that commercial fishing and the development of rich mineral deposits in the area have been hampered by lack of a suitable harbor. If the studies show the project would be successful, the AEC said, the atomic excavation could take place in 1960.

The author found Russia to be a land of paradoxes, the result of trying to cram into 40 years what it took Western nations over 100 to accomplish

"This is it," I thought as we rolled slowly over the bridge spanning the Bug River—1200 miles and 12 frontier posts from London, which we had left four days before. A Russian sentry at the barrier, his carbine shoulder-slung under a raincoat, eyed the GM-built Vauxhall Victor. "Wait here," he indicated.

An ambulance arrived from nowhere and deposited a young man. "Good afternoon," he greeted us in English. "I am your interpreter from Intourist (the Soviet travel agency). Call me Vladimir," he said, climbing into the back seat. "Follow that car." And we were off on our motor trip to Moscow.

The ambulance led the way into Brest, four miles away, whose busy railway station is Russia's westernmost mainline terminal. Although taken aback by this informal penetration of the last iron curtain of all, we had more surprises to come.

Upstairs, in a large room with tasseled velvet drapes and plush armchairs reminiscent of Grandma's front parlor, a serious youth from Intourist explained that there was no customs inspection. We merely had to sign a declaration that we carried no opium, hashish or live

Reflections on a Drive

In central Moscow and other large cities the streets are broad and well-surfaced

ammunition! He waved aside our carnet (the international travel document that permits temporary importation of cars without paying duty), and presented another form on which we promised to take the car out of the country when we left.

Our passports were quickly stamped and we bought some gasoline coupons at 50 cents a gallon. We then bolted a hearty midafternoon meal at the station restaurant, and 22-year-old Vladimir, assigned to us for the duration, said "Let's go."

First stop was at Brest's fuel depot, where 25 liters of 74-octane "premium" gas were pumped into the tank. Prepared for this, we'd had the Victor fitted with a 6.8 to 1 compression head at the factory in England. Once on the road again, Vladimir gave us a small route plan with instructions printed in English.

Moscow, we saw, was 635 miles ahead, and on the way were only 14 towns and six filling stations. The vision of wide-open spaces came to life as we sped eastward. The broad, tree-lined road sweeps through the flat countryside on the edge of the Pripet Marshes, and you can drive miles without seeing a person or house.

Roadside views are of brown fields reaching to the horizon, peat bogs and occasional signs in the strange Russian letters. The Victor purred on sweetly at a steady 60, slipping by a truck or horse-drawn wagon at long intervals. We were headed for Minsk, 210 miles from the border, our scheduled stop for the night.

Through Russia   by David Scott

Most side roads are poorly paved, and cars take a beating on the cobblestone

Century-old houses still stand in the shadow of new apartments

But, as darkness fell, this sparse traffic became a real hazard. The first hazy form caught in our headlights suddenly became an unlit wagon, and the scream of our tires woke the peasant asleep at the reins. After this near escape we cut the speed to about 45 and flicked on the piercing spotlight.

The wisdom of this precaution was demonstrated a few minutes later when we eased past several logs lying in the road. Beyond them were splintered wooden boards, and finally a dead horse—but no trace of the vehicle that had apparently plowed into the cart.

There was no warning of a section of road under repair, and only sharp braking prevented us from sailing into a sea of mud and rocks. Signs were inadequate, and the few reflecting signs were aimed at the wrong angle to catch oncoming lights. It was no joke driving now, and we felt intense relief when the lights of Minsk finally appeared.

Dinner at the best hotel in town was ample, and Vladimir helped us choose dishes like caviar and shashlik from the Russian menu. We ordered with relish, since Intourist was footing the bill. Actually, we had each paid in advance for 13 days at the rate of $11.25 a day. This covered the hotel, three meals and a traveling interpreter (full time, when away from his Moscow girl friend). Other expenses we paid in cash, but at a special tourist rate of exchange that gave us a ruble for 10 cents instead of the usual 25 cents. With that we could buy a bottle of beer for 35 cents and cigarettes at 10 cents a pack.

Our double room upstairs boasted more old-fashioned luxury, with heavy lace curtains, furniture upholstered in rich silk brocade, a marbled desk and a huge rubber plant. In strange contrast were the exposed plumbing, cold water and stopperless sink of the dingy, mirrorless bathroom. This was one of the many paradoxes of Soviet life that we were to find at every turn in this country that has tried to telescope into 40 years what advanced Western nations have taken over 100 to accomplish.

Example: Russia leads America in hurling a manmade satellite into space, but runs the inefficient side-valve engines that power most of its vehicles on 66-octane gas. With the Tu-104 it was the first country to have jet airliners in regular service, but relies on creaking wagons for much of its rural transport. Russia's production and variety of machine tools rivals that of America, but it gave up making ballpoint pens as a bad job, and consumer goods are generally shoddy, expensive and scarce.

More contrasts were seen in Minsk the next morning. This war-devastated city of 412,000 people has been rebuilt with imposing apartment houses and office blocks lining the broad avenues. But when we drove off the main street in a two-hour hunt for a gas pump that both worked and delivered the "high test" fuel, we bounced over bone-rattling cobbles in a road booby-trapped with flooded potholes, with manhole covers sticking two inches above the surface.

After a late start we dawdled along in the bright sunshine with photogenic clouds, and gave up all hope of reaching Moscow that night. The Minsk-Moscow highway stretches for 450 flat miles with scarcely a bend. It was possible to wind the Victor up to an effortless 75 miles per hour—safe, we thought, until an unexpected wavy spot tossed us against the roof. At first glance this road with no speed limit looks a natural for sports cars, but hard suspension here would be murder, and about 65 is top for steady cruising.

Driving through this vastness, so like the American great plains, we saw many places where grain was spread out across half the width of the road to dry in the sun. The wake of passing traffic blows away

In the field of aviation, Russia is modern, has jets in regular service

These new apartments are part of a housing project being built near Moscow

the chaff. Sometimes even small threshing machines were parked and running on the asphalt. Trucks were used to crush flax by driving them back and forth across it.

Our companions of the road were long-distance coaches that seat 32 people in comfort, and use a 180-horsepower supercharged diesel mounted at the rear to thunder along at close to 70. Few passenger cars were seen, and the traffic consisted mostly of gas-engined four-ton trucks. These are the stalwarts of Russian transport, and carry everything from timber and cows to mountainous loads of hay and up to 30 farm workers packed in like sardines.

They take a terrific beating from both overloading and tortuous roads, and we saw several trucks with dislocated axles rolling with a crablike movement. Once a four-tonner with recapped tires shed a large chunk of loose tread right in our path. Garages are widely spaced in Russia, and every truck driver is both trained and equipped to make major repairs on the spot. More than once we saw a roadside replacement of a broken spring or half shaft. These trucks are really run into the ground. I was told that they normally do 120,000 miles before a major overhaul, and are kept going for up to 500,000.

Truck drivers take a break at the rare gas stations along the highway, and the bright red Victor always attracted a crowd when it pulled in to refuel. They were tough, roughly dressed men, but always ready to talk and be helpful. At one place where no air was available, a gruff driver brought his truck over, attached a hose to his compressor and inflated our tires.

We had been two days in Russia, two days of driving down a broad, virtually empty highway. After a stopover at Smolensk we headed once more for our goal, that city of paradoxes, Moscow.

Midafternoon of this third day brought a change of scenery. About 30 miles from Moscow we started seeing clusters of houses. Most of them were wooden shanties, but every one had a TV antenna. Occasionally we'd pass a factory. At the city outskirts, huge apartment houses stood amid a forest of building cranes. Then the traffic really started —few cars, but an endless stream of green trucks.

Moskvitch cars are turned off the assembly line at an average of 185 a day

New impressions tumbled in. The road was being sprinkled by water tankers, then swept by mechanical brushes to clean up the muddy tracks deposited by trucks from adjacent building sites. Vladimir told us you can be fined for driving a dirty car in Moscow. It's also an offense to blow your horn or drop a cigarette butt in the street.

Our first stop on this broad belt of concrete was for a bewildering set of four traffic lights. Normally you can turn right on red, but a left-turn is allowed only on a double green light. Overhead hung a row of circular signs indicating lanes, prohibited vehicles, permitted turns and other regulations. The usual system for left-turns on main avenues is to proceed straight across an intersection to the U-turn sign halfway up the block, then swing around into the oncoming traffic and cut across to be in position for the next right-turn.

In the center of the city there's a running battle between cars and pedestrians, although the Muscovite walker (usually runner) stranded in midstream has enough sense to stand dead still as the traffic rushes past him. It's a rat race to the uninitiated, but the militiamen (Russian for cops) seem unconcerned. Immaculately garbed in military-type uniforms, they often control traffic merely with a jerk of the head or repeated whistle blasts. Experiencing this continuous war of man vs. machine, we recalled the laconic advice of the English-language guide to motorists in the U.S.S.R.: "When necessary, the car should be stopped in time to avoid an accident."

At the vast permanent Agricultural and Industrial Exhibition in Moscow we had a close look at the cars the Russian can buy. Most popular is the four-seater Moskvitch, similar in appearance to more than one British model and costing the ruble equivalent of $1500. This represents more than one year's average wages and must be paid in cash—there's no consumer credit. Outwardly the car is conventional, with integral body-chassis, a 35-horsepower L-head engine and three-speed manual transmission. Radio and heater are standard.

Beneath the surface the Moskvitch bristles with features that reflect the arduous Soviet driving conditions and weather. For example, the engine has two separate oil filters and a radiator shutter. A towing hook is fitted in case you get bogged down, and the seats fold flat to form a double bed for when you're stranded miles from nowhere. The toolkit would equip a small garage, including no fewer than 20 different wrenches.

We also had a look at the larger Volga that sells for $3000. It is powered by one of Russia's first overhead-valve gas engines—a four-cylinder unit rated at 70 horsepower. Initially it was to have an automatic transmission, but this gave so much trouble that the idea was shelved. It is a pleasantly styled machine—a compromise between American and European designs.

A visit to the Moskvitch plant gave us a glimpse of how the Soviets make cars. Daily output there is 185, amounting to half the country's total annual production of 110,000 units. Machinery is modern by European standards with a considerable number of automatic transfer lines for the engine block and cylinder head, manifold, transmission housing and other large components. Automation is applied widely to special-purpose machines for making smaller parts such as pistons and universal joints.

Russia's production figure for trucks is more impressive, since the country's transport system relies heavily on fleets of rugged machines. Almost all these trucks are heavy-duty jobs with pay-load ratings from 2½ to 40 tons, and current output is some 370,000 a year. Although this is only about half of America's production in the same load category, it is over three times the combined output of Britain, West Germany and France.

At the ZIL plant in Moscow we saw one four-tonner or a heavier six-by-six version rolling off the assembly lines every 2½ minutes. Over 20 automatic lines are used for machining engine and transmission parts, and production is keyed to a high pitch. In addition to trucks the factory turns out 11 coaches a day, with 1500 bicycles and 30 refrigerators as sidelines. I was struck by the number of women workers (nearly a third of the 40,000 employees), and especially by the way they held every type of man's job.

I had another glimpse of this scientific fervor when I visited the offices of *Tekhnika Molodezhi (Technology for the Young)*. Backed by state funds, this monthly has a half-million circulation—limited only by paper supplies. It presents advanced developments, such as in nuclear physics or high-speed metal-cutting with ceramic tools, in simple terms and with humorous cartoons. A few years ago science fiction was shunned as "unrealistic," but now there is a special "Fantastic Editor" concerned with stories about rocketships and interplanetary travel.

The last thing we saw on the Moscow sky line as we drove westward was the tower above the 32-story "Palace of Science"—claimed to be the tallest building in Europe. This is the new university, conceived on a massive scale with 150 lecture halls and 1000 laboratories to take care of 17,000 students. But the paradoxes of Russia re-emerged with the first sight of the wooden shacks and broken-down trucks.

Politics aside, this country with nearly three times the area of America appears to have the pioneering spirit of the Midwest 100 years ago, along with a massive appetite for 20th-century technology.

Around the world more acres are being put under cultivation as

Farm Machines Race the Population

By Rafe Gibbs

In Cuba, the old and new work side by side handling loads of sugar cane at a plantation

The Kenya native, his dust-caked face cracked by a big grin, reached into the bag slung at his waist and produced a gleaming new carburetor. Handing it to the "boss man" of the farmstead, he said, "Tractor walk again."

And so it would—after being idle for 12 days while the native waited for the carburetor to come from Nairobi. It was an unimportant incident perhaps, but it told the story: Progress through mechanization and modern scientific methods—with setbacks.

"The world's farmers today are producing 20 percent more food and agricultural products than 20 years ago," reports Wilhelm Anderson of the U. S. Department of Agriculture's Foreign Service. Then he adds: "The increase is nearly as great as the increase in the world's population."

The race between food production and the birth rate has not been won—not by a long way, particularly in the Far East. World population today stands at 2.7 billion—23 percent above prewar level, as compared with agriculture's 20 percent increase. But, for the first time in many years, economists are seeing real hope that the gap may be closed eventually.

In 1938-39, there were only 2.6 million tractors scattered around

A naked youngster watches as one of the 152,000 tractors in Africa goes by

the world. Perhaps the word "scattered," however, would not apply to North America, because it had 1.7 million of those tractors. The Soviet had 500,000; Europe, 300,000, and all of the rest of the world only 100,000.

By 1955—the latest figure year for which international figures are available—the world total had made the astounding jump to 7.6 million, and this figure does not include the Soviet Union, which is not reporting. North and Central America had five million tractors; Europe, nearly two million; Oceania, 270,000; South America, 158,000; Africa, 152,000 and Asia, 70,000.

Several years ago, we were riding in a car with J. H. Tippett of Clarkston, Wash., one of the Northwest's biggest cattle producers, when we came upon a tractor turning new pasture land at one of his ranches.

"That," said Tippett, pointing to the tractor, "is science's most important gift to the rancher."

"Because it turned the horse out to pasture?"

"Well, it did that all right. But, more important, you can use it as a bulldozer—and build roads."

That fact is accounting for much of the booming agriculture output, particularly in such countries as Australia.

If a ghost rider out of Texas' past should prod his phantom cayuse today into the back-range country of Australia, he would think he was living again while cattle were dying—or at least growing mighty lean on the trail. He could sneeze from the dust of bawling herds, market-bound on their own power that was growing weaker between water holes. He could see cattle that had left the home range as good beef being sold at the end of the grueling overland trek for poor beef.

But, as new roads are built and trucks roll on them, this practice is gradually fading. As a result of this and other factors, Australia's farm output is 22 percent above the 1935-39 level.

Man without the machines today in some areas just barely lives. Take, for instance, this recent report to the United Nations by Felisberto C. De Camargo on Brazil's Amazon regions where tractor-tread marks would send the natives scurrying back into the jungles:

"Here in this enchanting paradise that is the New World, a large part of the people cannot obtain more than 1000 calories of food daily. The people are able to live, however, thanks to the calories they receive from the sun, which compensate for the calories that do not reach their bodies from food."

This situation, however, is not true of Brazil as a whole or of Latin America as a whole. Excluding Argentina, Latin America shows a rise in agricultural output since prewar days of nearly two thirds. Argentina's agricultural output has dropped in recent years because, shortly after the war, governmental policy favored industry over agriculture. This policy is now changing, and agricultural output in Argentina is expected to increase to a great degree.

U. S. Foreign Agricultural Service reports show that the Dominican Republic, Colombia and Panama, all net importers of rice just after the war, now grow all their requirements. But what has happened in Mexico is probably most startling.

A wealthy Georgia cotton planter, touring a rural area of Mexico with his wife recently, commented to a Mexican guide, "You know, my wife figured she could pick up some information on early Aztec history, but maybe I can pick up some information on modern cotton raising."

In the last 20 years, Mexico has increased cotton production more than five times, and Mexican cotton is now an important factor on the international market. Mexico's wheat crop for 1956—about 40 million bushels—was up 50 percent over that of 1947. Mexico used to import about 15 million bushels of wheat a year from the United States, but now United States imports have stopped almost entirely. Other crops, such as corn and livestock, are slated for big increases in the near future.

Twenty years ago, Mexico's irrigation projects were barely worth mentioning. Today, irrigated land totals 5.3 million acres.

Africa can also make its boasts. Example: Kenya produced nearly 425,000 bags of coffee in the 1955-56 crop season—nearly double that of the previous year. But even more significant in Kenya is the development of African-owned coffee acreage. In 1951, it totaled only 1725 acres. By 1955 it had increased to 7759, with nearly 30,000 licensed growers. Under the territory's expansion plan, the goal is

With irrigation, Mexico has jumped cotton production 5 times in 20 years

71,500 acres by 1968, surpassing the present European-owned coffee acreage of 59,000.

In Asia there is progress too, but in that great area with its masses of people it is more difficult to pinpoint the spectacular. And there is always China—vast, hungry China. Communist leaders are making speeches about how they are mechanizing the country's agriculture. Mechanization will no doubt come there—but slowly. Two-wheeled, double-shared plows and new water wheels have been put out in quantity. Tractors have been shipped in from Russia. But a village leader sadly shook his grey head after viewing a government tractor demonstration, and said:

"It is wonderful. But so much of our land is fit only for humans to work—and they need the work so badly."

India has similar problems, but there more emphasis is being given to increased irrigation, fertilization and development of new land. By 1961, India plans to raise irrigated areas from 67 million to 88 million acres, boost the use of nitrogenous fertilizer from 685,000 short tons to 2 million, and conduct land reclamation and improvement projects on 3.5 million acres. India's goal for the next five years: a 28-percent increase in agricultural output.

The United States is responsible for much of the world development in agriculture by providing funds, equipment and know-how. The State Department's Point Four program has been effective. It is still too early to measure just how effective, but the comments of Dr. James E. Kraus, Dean of the University of Idaho's College of Agriculture, which has been administering the program in Ecuador, are typical.

"Adapting Idaho research on poultry, Ecuador has a new commercial industry in broiler production," said Dean Kraus. "Eight-week-old fryers are finding a steady market."

Almost a "coals to Newcastle" incident was observed in the extensive potato fertilizer and variety trials Dr. George Woodbury, head of horticulture at Idaho and leader of the Ecuador unit, has instituted near Quito. His trials are near the area where the potato originated. Yet research results from Idaho show great promise of helping get more and better potatoes in that country.

And how is all this world agricultural development affecting this country?

Well, just remember that the world's agricultural output has not yet caught up with the increase in population. Through world political developments, our customers have changed, but we have more of them —and our surpluses have been shrinking.

Even though you can find modern farm equipment operating today in darkest Africa, it will be a long time before agriculture throughout the world reaches the point of mechanical intensification and efficiency in the United States. It will be a long time before you will see a scene beyond our borders such as the one we witnessed the other day in Oregon.

Our car was stopped at a highway rail crossing, and we sat and sat as 90 flatcars passed before us. Each car was loaded with three combines, making the total 270. All were headed for the same destination —the town of Pendleton—to be fanned out from there to regional farming areas.

DC-3s dropped thousands of paratroopers and tons of supplies during WW II

THE SAGA OF THE DC-3

This remarkable airplane has spanned almost half the history of flight; its indestructible nature has been the source of countless legends

By Joseph Stocker

They called the airplane "Whistling Willie, the Flying Sieve." It happened in China during World War II when Jap strafers caught a DC-3 on the ground and riddled it with machine-gun fire. Coolies patched up about 1000 holes with pieces of canvas.

Then it took off for India with 61 refugees aboard, a plane that was intended—under normal circumstances—to carry 21 passengers and a crew of three.

En route the plane ran into a tropical storm. Rain loosened the canvas patches and wind passing over the holes caused a variety of shrill whistles which increased until the ship sounded like a thousand screaming banshees.

For two hours the intrepid airplane lumbered through hostile skies. Finally it landed. As its weary pilot swung to the ground, an Army major on the base came up to him and growled, "Why did you bother to radio ahead? We could hear you 50 miles away!"

To old-time pilots familiar with the DC-3 and its Herculean capabilities, this incident probably won't seem unusual. They've long since regarded the "gooney bird," one of their affectionate nicknames for the DC-3, as the world's toughest, longest-lived and most unconquerable airplane—an airplane that refuses to die.

It was in 1936—more than two decades ago—that the DC-3 was born. As the most efficient and economical transport produced up to that time, it revolutionized air travel.

Then came the Martins, Convairs, DC-4s, 6s and 7s, the "Connies" and "Super Connies," the "Stratocruisers" and the Viscount jet-props and, more recently, the jet transports. By all the rules of a fast-moving business, the DC-3 should have been obsolete and gone from the skies long ago. After all, how many 1936-model automobiles are still operating today?

But the old gooney bird isn't about to vanish. Of the 10,926 DC-3s manufactured by the Douglas Aircraft Co., some 4500 are still flying throughout the world. Thirty-four scheduled airlines in the U.S. and 113 foreign airlines are still using them. Additional hundreds are in use by non-scheduled carriers, private operators and the military of many nations. In both hemispheres, over countries civilized and not-so-civilized, gooney birds fly every day, carrying cargoes that range from coal to cattle and fish to flowers, not to mention, of course, people. And in Russia, where just about everything is claimed to have been invented, the plane most generally used for commercial travel is the Ilyushin LI-2, the Soviet version of the DC-3.

However, it's right here in the gooney bird's own native country that its accomplishments have become immortalized in aviation history. During World War II, despite the fact that it was already outdated, it proved to be both a hero and an almost indestructible workhorse. Even in the first desperate days of Korea, it flew tons of supplies to enable a thin line of defenders to check the unexpected Communist thrust. And during the peace years it carried America into the Air Age, spawned the cut-rate aircoach and airfreight era and gave more people their first ride in an airplane than anything else on wings.

Indestructible? Well, consider the DC-3 airliner over Arizona that was caught in a violent downdraft. More than 10 feet of its 95-foot wingspan was sheared off in flight when it struck the ground. But the pilot brought his storm-buffeted plane and passengers in for a safe landing.

It seems that other extreme weather conditions can't keep this airplane from flying, either. The Air Force abandoned one on a high glacier in Iceland when huge snow drifts almost swallowed it up. But some young Icelanders, operators of a small airline, bought it as salvage for $1600. The next spring they found that the snow, as it dried and froze, had shrunk away from the DC-3, leaving it as well-preserved as if it had been "mothballed." So they simply tractored a runway across the snow, climbed aboard, started and warmed the engines and took off. As far as the Air Force knows, that bird is still flying.

The gooney bird, or "Dizzy Three," as it's sometimes called, had its origin in a letter. It was a brief, two-paragraph note written in 1932 by Jack Frye, then vice-president of Transcontinental and Western Airlines, to Donald Douglas in Santa Monica, Calif. Would Douglas be

This one returned to the air after New Guinea natives dragged it from the jungle

interested in designing an air transport capable of carrying 12 passengers? Although occupied mainly with military airplanes, he decided to give it a whirl, resulting in the DC-1 (the letters stood for Douglas Commercial).

The DC-1 was a success. It flew from Winslow, Ariz., to Albuquerque, N. Mex., on one engine and broke 19 world's records. But only a single prototype was built. Even while it was being tested, Douglas went to work refining and enlarging it, and the result was the DC-2, a 14-passenger ship.

It, too, was a success. Don Douglas built 138 of them and might have kept right on building them except American Airlines thought he could do even better. What they wanted was a larger and more luxurious airliner.

Thus was born the DC-3, a 21-seater. "That figure 21," says a Douglas official, "was one of the happiest, luckiest figures we ever hit on."

Powered by two 900-horsepower Wright Cyclone engines, the plane was safer and easier to fly than any other transport then in existence, and its pay load was one third greater. It cruised at 185 miles per hour and could clip off 210 in a pinch. Where other transports had to fly through storms, the DC-3 could fly over them. It had two separate sets of instruments in the cockpit, each independent of the other in case one failed. And, best of all, it had "George," the brand-new automatic pilot developed by the Sperry Gyroscope Co.

An eccentricity of the gooney bird, however, disturbed the pilots. The plane's wings had a slight but clearly visible tendency to flap while in flight. Accordingly, the pilots gave it another nickname, the "Flying Vagrant" (no means of support).

But their apprehension was soon relieved when they learned that the Douglas engineers had built this into the plane to relieve structural wing tension. In fact, one of the early DC-3s was flown into what appeared to be an innocent accumulation of clouds. But inside was a freak downdraft so severe that passenger seats tore bolts from the floor. Yet the plane made it and afterwards no structural defects could be found.

This wing tension feature proved to be a major reason for the plane's extraordinary durability.

Don Douglas originally thought he would produce only 50 gooney birds. Then, when airline presidents began lining up at his office door, he revised his estimate and calculated that he might be able to sell 500. He doubted then if the market would absorb much more.

But he didn't figure on a second world war.

When it broke out, the Allies desperately needed air transports. Manufacturers were already making four-engine planes, but they weren't far enough along yet. The DC-3, on the other hand, was in business. Its "bugs" had long since been ironed out. And so orders poured in at Douglas, and DC-3s poured off the assembly lines, hastily donned their wartime coats of olive drab and flew off to the war.

Dressed in this uniform, with its familiar "bucket" seats, the DC-3 was known variously as the "Three," "Old Fatso," the "Doug," the C-47 (Air Force version), R4D (Navy) and the Dakota (British). Years later a well-known general named Eisenhower called it something else. He said it had been one of the most valuable weapons of the war.

It was truly that. It hauled men and supplies to every battle front and brought back litters of wounded. It re-opened the life line into China by hurdling the Hump in some of the worst weather on the face of the globe. It dumped paratroopers behind enemy lines and pulled gliders full of troops. It was shot at and shot up, and still it flew.

One gooney bird set some kind of a record by taking off from Burma with 74 people aboard, including Jimmy Doolittle, on his way home after bombing Tokyo. The ship had been airborne just a few minutes when Doolittle poked his head into the cockpit. "If I'd known you were crazy enough to try to fly this thing with this many people aboard," he said, "I'd have walked home."

They'll fly from water as well as land as this converted model illustrates

The exigencies of wartime forced fliers to do quite a number of things with the gooney bird that would have given Douglas engineers the willies if they'd known. The ship had been designed, for instance, to carry a maximum load of 25,000 pounds. But pilots couldn't always afford this luxury. For example, when 27 DC-3s crossed the South Atlantic in 1942, bound for the Hump in history's first mass ocean flight, they lurched off the runway with 35,000 pounds each.

On at least one occasion the gooney bird was used as a bomber. Some Air Force pilots, tired of being sitting ducks for Japanese anti-aircraft fire over the Hump, loaded up one night with old carbide and gasoline drums, plus a few fortifying fingers of alcoholic "jungle juice." Then they flew over a Jap airfield in Burma, unloaded their homemade bombs, fired Tommy guns and carbines through the cockpit windows and flew merrily home. They were court-martialed for unauthorized use of government equipment and really didn't care.

When the war ended, four-engine airplanes were the vogue. Douglas produced its last DC-3 in 1946 for a Brazilian airline, and figured that was about the end of the old gooney bird.

But they figured wrong again. For, instead of going to the junk heaps, war-surplus DC-3s were snatched up by the thousands, at bargain prices, and put back into operation. Feeder lines bought many of them and opened up rural America to air travel. They've been in operation ever since.

This is explained to some extent by the fact that the gooney bird can get into and out of short landing strips. And these predominate in many remote parts of the world, especially South America, Asia and Africa. Thus, the DC-3 is—and, for a long time will continue to be—the backbone of air travel in those regions. As one pilot put it: "Millions of people in South America were familiar with the DC-3 before they ever saw an automobile. Two thirds of the people in Central America have had their traveling eyeteeth cut on the DC-3, but have never ridden on a train nor seen one."

Every now and then there's talk of some new twin-engine transport which, it is confidently said, will supplant the DC-3. But so far it hasn't been replaced.

The reason is partly its stubborn sturdiness. "You can wreck one," said a pilot, "but you can't wear it out." Yet the reason is also economic. Most of the Threes now in use were picked up as surplus, for a few thousand dollars, and have been written off the books as fully depreciated. Replacements are expensive. The average operator isn't going to spend big money on new ships and sweep his DC-3s out of their hangars so long as he can keep 'em flying.

Meanwhile, Douglas has compiled some interesting statistics on them. They've flown, as nearly as can be estimated, about 87 *billion* passenger miles and some 75 *million* hours. They've carried 400 million commercial passengers, or approximately the population of India. These figures do not include military operations. And DC-3s still comprise about 35 percent of the world's air-transport fleet and do all types of other jobs, from radar-testing to pest-control forest-spraying.

Here doing a time-lapse study of pollen, Ott focuses 25 cameras on ragweed

Millions of televiewers look on John Ott as an old friend, always on hand to help them tackle their gardening problems. Millions of movie fans look on John Ott as a magician with a camera.

A few men—biologists, pathologists, chemists and other scientists—look on John Ott as a founder of new scientific technique. And only this handful has seen his most significant work.

These scientists, usually unemotional in their approach, have gasped at the sights he has shown them. Vital life processes which occur over a period of days, weeks or months unfold on a movie screen in seconds. They watch cancer cells divide and redivide, ragweed pollen react in the nasal secretion of a hay-fever victim. They watch light of certain wavelengths determine the sex of various plants.

They watch these spectacular sights through the magic of time-lapse motion pictures, taken through a high-power microscope.

John Ott is a pioneer of time-lapse photography. Today his time-lapse cameras are spying on living cells. In his basement laboratory at Winnetka, Ill., he speeds the passage of time a hundred-thousandfold.

Back in 1927 a 17-year-old lad bought a movie camera. First off, he decided he'd photograph the unfolding of apple blossoms on the tree in the front yard. To do the job, he figured he'd have to expose one frame of film every few minutes. Then when he projected the film the blossom would unfold before his eyes. This was to be just the opposite

He Brings Life's Secrets into Focus

John Ott pioneered time-lapse photography with his movies of flowers bursting into bloom. Now his cameras are helping scientists learn more about cancer cells

By Clifford B. Hicks

of slow-motion photography. What he was going to do was speed things up.

His first try showed blossoms appearing and disappearing so fast he scarcely could see them. After several false starts he produced his first successful time-lapse sequence. On the screen, buds appeared, swelled and burst into spectacular bloom.

That was 30 years ago. The boy grew to be John Ott, Chicago banker, who puttered around taking films of his garden as a hobby. Because the time-lapse technique was new, he had to devise his own equipment, and finally succeeded in making it automatic. After any desired interval, timers would close the shutters in his greenhouse, snap on floodlights, expose one frame of film, turn off the lights and open the shutters again.

Soon Walt Disney became interested in Ott's time-lapse films. As a result the films have appeared in the Disney movies *Secrets of Life* and *Nature's Half Acre,* and on the Disneyland television show. (Recently Ott rephotographed the blossoming of an apple tree in his yard, this time for Disney. A lad appeared in this film, too—Ott's son.) Ott also has shown his films on such TV shows as *Zoo Parade, Today, The Home Show* and *Out on the Farm.*

He is a man of incredible patience. When he wanted to show the formation of a bunch of bananas on the screen, he trained 10 cameras on a banana tree for 18 months. In a recent study of ragweed he had

25 cameras focused on the ragweed plants, some of them watching the formation of pollen through microscopes.

Scientists peering through microscopes always have had difficulty in observing certain phenomena. Some activities, such as the splitting of cells, occur at unpredictable moments.

"Similarly, a biologist trying to observe a vital life process often is frustrated because he can't actually watch it occur. The change is just too slow. In such a situation, a time-lapse movie is ideal. In minutes we can show a life process from beginning to end. We simply speed it up."

Ott has designed his own equipment to speed up life. In his miniature laboratory for science studies, a high-intensity light is focused through the microscope slide. The microscope itself is a new phase-contrast type that splits the light beam, retarding part of the light. The result is much finer definition (important to photographic work) and no need for staining the specimen. The staining process frequently kills living specimens.

A special eyepiece on the microscope permits Ott to watch the specimen at the same time a frame of the film is being exposed. Whenever Ott refocuses the microscope, the camera automatically moves too. He also has installed miniature motors which will move the microscope slide at the infinitesimal speed of $\frac{1}{5000}$ *inch per hour.*

Heart of the time-lapse system, of course, is the timer, which can be preset to expose one frame of film automatically at any interval from 10 seconds to 90 minutes.

Perhaps the most spectacular of Ott's new scientific films shows individual grains of pollen fertilizing flowers. Before your eyes the grain of pollen produces a tube and through it the contents of the pollen are discharged into the stigma. Ordinary time-lapse movies go on from there to show a pollinated pumpkin flower developing into a full-size pumpkin in 30 seconds, changing from green to bright orange.

Another time-lapse study shows the effects of ragweed pollen on humans. Across the screen move spheres of pollen. They are swimming through the nasal secretion of a person who is *not* allergic. Nothing happens. Then similar pollen grains appear, this time in a culture taken

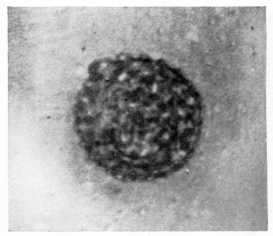 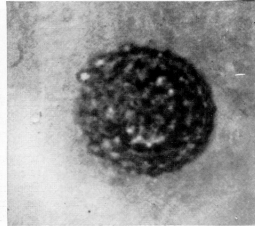

from a sniffling hay-fever victim. Almost immediately the pollen starts emitting tiny drops of liquid. Until this film was available there was some doubt as to whether the pollen itself changed, or whether the only change occurred in the nasal passage of the hay-fever victim. The time-lapse films prove that the ragweed pollen emits some substance. It's a film of profound significance in the study of such allergies.

Ott has become intrigued with the effect of certain wavelengths of light on plants. Light in a particular band will cause certain plants to produce flowers of only one sex. For example, a pumpkin exposed to a certain wavelength will produce all female flowers. The same plant, exposed to another wavelength, will produce all male flowers. Ott now is analyzing the effects of bands of light on the sex of fish, and there is some evidence that certain wavelengths have a strong effect. Biologists are so interested they already are asking him to make similar studies on poultry and cattle. The implications are obvious.

Another time-lapse study shows cancer cells dividing. One of the principal characteristics of malignant cells is that they reproduce wildly. Ott's films, of great interest to scientists studying the cause or causes of cancer, actually show the division of cancer cells in such detail you can even see the chromosomes ("threads" which carry the hereditary genes) lining up in orderly fashion prior to the division.

For Northwestern University, Ott set his cameras to spying on the life secrets of cancer cells for a full year. He imprisoned malignant-tumor cells inside a glass cage, and rigged pipes to the prison which fed nourishment in the form of plasma and saline solution to the vigorously growing cells. His cameras took one exposure every 30 seconds, day and night, for a year. In that year he obtained 1,041,200 separate pictures on 65,075 feet of film, certainly the most intensive study ever made of cancer.

Ott makes no pretense of being a specialist in this microscopic world, and makes it clear that he leaves the interpretation of his films to qualified scientists. There is a universal desire on their part to lay their hands on more of his work. In the time he has been showing his microscopic studies, he has been besieged by universities and medical laboratories to tackle specific assignments.

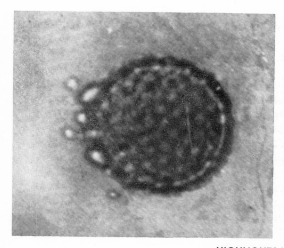

Ott's film shows how ragweed pollen, exposed to the nasal secretion of a hay-fever sufferer, starts emitting tiny drops of liquid

The IGY has substantially
added to our knowledge
of the planet earth and
the universe around it

What We've
Learned
From the IGY

By Clifford B. Hicks

For 18 months, some 10,000 scientists from 67 nations worked 'round the clock on the world's biggest and best-publicized research project. In ships, planes and on foot they moved across the earth's surface from pole to pole, plumbed new depths of the ocean, sent balloons and rockets to record altitudes and fired satellites into whirling orbits around the globe.

IGY scientists have recorded millions of observations. What have they learned so far in their research studies? Here are just a few of their discoveries:

The earth does not move through "empty" space. As a matter of fact, evidence indicates that it exists "inside" the sun, never leaving the corona, the fourth and outermost layer of the sun's gaseous atmosphere.

There are indications that the earth's own atmosphere extends at least 8000 miles into space; scientists formerly believed it extended 250 to 500 miles at the most.

Quite likely there are great and previously unsuspected magnetic fields in outer space.

There may be an enormous "electrojet"—a vast river of electrical current—flowing around the earth at its magnetic equator.

Auroras stage their eerily beautiful shows simultaneously in both hemispheres, as though controlled by a single gigantic switch.

Some 10,000 feet below the Gulf Stream is a swift current of water running in the opposite direction.

Antarctica may not be a single land mass, but a group of islands buried beneath an eternal blanket of ice three times the thickness previously believed.

The earth is perhaps the most difficult scientific specimen ever studied. Too big to investigate in its entirety, it can only be examined

This drawing of the earth shows some of the important findings of the IGY:

1. Auroras occur simultaneously in both hemispheres;

2. Evidence indicates there is a vast river of electrical current flowing around the magnetic equator;

3. Cosmic rays vary precisely with latitude;

4. About 10,000 feet below the Gulf Stream is a swift current of water running in the opposite direction;

5. Antarctica may be a group of islands buried under a blanket of ice much thicker than it was formerly believed to be;

6. There are vast magnetic fields of unknown origin in outer space;

7. Eerie "whistler" radio signals set off by thunderstorms in one hemisphere can be heard in the other;

8. Man can launch artificial moons as tools to learn more about the earth;

9. Preliminary findings of Explorer I indicate that man, with proper equipment, can exist in outer space.

piecemeal. So far, at least, man has been bound to its surface, unable to climb out into space for an over-all look. This reluctant specimen, earth, is a strange, misshapen mass, squashed in at its poles, bulging at its belly, pockmarked with grotesque warts and wrinkles, wobbling on its axis, its crust heaving up and down in great earth tides.

Here are some IGY discoveries, starting from the vastness of space and progressing inward toward the center of the earth:

Cosmic rays, as they pass through space toward the earth, apparently are deflected. A theory has been advanced that their strange trajectories are due to huge and previously unsuspected fields of unknown origin, far out in space, which are somewhat similar to the magnetic field around the earth.

For the first time auroras have been studied concurrently in both hemispheres. Scientists of 49 countries have participated in this auroral research. Their observations not only show that auroras occur simultaneously in both hemispheres, but can be seen in tropical areas much oftener than previously suspected. For example, since IGY began, three great auroras have been sighted in Havana, Cuba.

As a result of rocket studies, scientists have discovered that the sun fires bursts of short and powerful X rays at the earth, which penetrate to within 30 miles of the surface. Rocket investigations also show that there are more than 10,000,000 electrons per cubic inch at an altitude of 105 miles, a density much greater than previously believed.

Systematically flying and sailing cosmic-ray instruments around the world, scientists have pinned down the "cosmic-ray equator"—the line representing the minimum number of cosmic rays—and found that,

Research on the ionosphere was carried on during the IGY in this aircraft

Here a camera is being lowered to the ocean floor

strangely enough, it departs significantly from the earth's magnetic equator. Cosmic rays vary so greatly with latitude that scientists can detect a latitude change as small as seven miles merely by observing the frequency of the rays.

The "electrojet" is a great river of electric current girdling the equator. There are probably similar enormous electrical currents high above the magnetic poles. It has been suggested that someday man might tap these incredible electric currents as sources of power for space conquest.

The mysterious "whistlers" have come in for their share of research. Whistlers first were recognized as a natural phenomenon during World War I, when the German scientist Barkhausen set up radio equipment to try to eavesdrop on Allied military messages. Occasionally he heard an eerie, descending whistle of unknown origin. These ghostly sounds have baffled scientists for years.

Recent research indicates that a whistler is a radio signal touched off by a lightning stroke. It has been theorized that the radio signal swings out into space for thousands of miles along the earth's magnetic lines, then curves back, striking the earth's surface at a corresponding point on the opposite hemisphere. To test the theory, whistlerlike signals recently were transmitted from Annapolis, Md. They were detected at Cape Horn, precisely at the opposite end of one of the earth's magnetic lines.

In addition to pinning down the nature of whistlers, this research reveals, somewhat to the surprise of scientists, that the ion density and concentration of molecules along the whistler paths is much greater than formerly believed. In other words, part of the earth's atmosphere must extend thousands of miles into what was believed to be empty space. Actually, of course, this atmosphere is so tenuous it represents only stray molecules, ions and electrons.

Coming down to the surface of the earth: Antarctica, that coldest and most inaccessible of all areas, has been placed under planned study for the first time. Scientists of 12 nations manned 50 different stations on the frozen wastes. One weather record has fallen. On September 17, 1957, a meteorologist at the South Pole station jotted down the lowest temperature ever recorded—a crackling —102.1 degrees F. Weathermen at the bottom of the world have discovered a great, permanent cold-air mass, cyclonic in movement, over the central part of Antarctica. Quite likely it plays a vital role in the Southern Hemisphere's weather.

Consider the "continent" of Antarctica itself. There now is a ring of oil barrels (no barber pole!) marking the South Pole. Scientists recently set off three shots of high explosives near the barrels. Echoes of the shots showed that the ice at that point is 8297 feet deep, and rests on land rising 903 feet above sea level. However, at Byrd Station, a relatively short distance away, the land is 5000 feet below sea level, and the station itself squats on an ice cap 10,000 feet thick. Traverse recordings of Antarctica are now being made and may well reveal that the continent is a series of peaks thrusting up above sea level.

At the other end of the world, IGY teams were amazed when their sounding instruments suddenly revealed the existence of an unsuspected range of polar undersea mountains more than 5000 feet high. Though more research is required, scientists believe this tremendous ridge may form a barrier to the movement of polar waters. This, in turn, could influence the ocean currents of the Northern Hemisphere, the weather of half the world, and the refertilization of subarctic fisheries.

IGY scientists hauled an oil rig into Greenland and drilled more than 1400 feet into the ice to pull up ice cores. So great was the compression at that depth that some of the cores exploded as the compressed air in them expanded. Nevertheless the cores are a history book of the climate, for each layer shows the annual precipitation. The cores are studies like tree rings, and are expected to reveal the trends of the climate for past hundreds of years, and to help answer age-old questions regarding climatic cycles.

Oceanographers in the Atlantic sank "beeping buoys" to preset depths and tracked them as they drifted. Surprisingly, the buoys revealed a countercurrent beneath the Gulf Stream moving briskly along toward the southwest.

Earth tides were also investigated. The earth's crust thrusts up and falls back in a manner identical to tides of the ocean. Hawaii, for example, rises and falls four inches each day.

Perhaps the most significant discovery of IGY so far has been the revelation that men of all nations, even in these times of tension, can cooperate in a vast scientific undertaking. Though the Sputniks beat Explorer into orbit, there has been little chest-beating or rancor among the scientists themselves, who see the satellites primarily as tools for studying the earth's environment.

MEXICO'S GLAMOUR CAMPUS

Famed as a nation for its contemporary
architecture, Mexico has built a
university whose buildings are
among the world's finest

By Thomas E. Stimson, Jr.

*At top, the library is covered with
colorful mosaics. At right, a classroom with glass-wall construction*

Artists had to work from scaffolding on the medical building. The Aztec mosaic of glass tiles over its entrance tells a tale of Life and Death

North America's oldest university is, in some respects, the most modern. Its striking new buildings were conceived by Mexico's greatest architects and engineers and dedicated to the proposition that school buildings can be beautiful as well as useful.

The results are so spectacular that most visitors feel a real envy for the 25,000 students who study literature or engineering, architecture, medicine or other courses on the new campus.

The university traces its history back to 1551 when the "University of New Spain" was granted a charter by the King of Spain. Shortly afterward the name was changed to the "Royal and Pontifical University of Mexico" and was supported by endowments from Mexico's gold mines. The school was abolished during various revolutions, and in

Huge Olympic Stadium was designed to resemble the crater of a volcano. High sides give more of the spectators choice seats on the 50-yard line

Seating areas are reached through 48 tunnels. Below, three swimming pools are connected so casual swimmers can wander easily from one to the other

The entire end of one science building is a painted mural which depicts how knowledge has been created by combining bits from various civilizations

Bas-relief by famed artist Diego Rivera decorates side of stadium. It is made of scores of acid-stained rocks

Pavilion of Cosmic Rays houses neutron counters and ionization chambers

recent years has operated on funds from the sale of land grants. The present campus consists of more than 1500 acres of ancient lava flows, called the Pedregal, at the southern edge of Mexico City.

One of its buildings stands on stilts, its thin concrete roof pulled taut around the entire structure like the canvas of some ultramodern covered wagon. Beneath the roof, ionization chambers and automatic neutron counters keep a 24-hour watch on the cosmic rays that strike through the thin concrete with virtually no interference.

The building is the Pavilion of Cosmic Rays at the University of Mexico. In a way, it symbolizes the rest of the campus, for here, blazing with color, are some of the most unique school buildings ever to welcome a student.

The campus represents the largest single construction project in Mexico since ancient times and was built at record speed. It was started in 1950 during the regime of President Miguel Aleman, and a huge statue of him stands at one end of the main esplanade. Most of the buildings are of the modern "international" style. The stadium and some of the sports facilities are deliberately styled to resemble Mexico's volcanoes and her ancient Indian pyramids.

The magnificent new stadium is suitable for football and for all track and field events. Authorities hope Mexico will be chosen as host for one of the future World Olympic Games. Some coaches don't believe sea-level athletes could put on a good show in the 7500-foot elevation of Mexico City, but Mexicans explain that almost anyone becomes acclimatized after about 10 days in the thin air. Most Olympic teams spend that much time in practice at the scene of the games. The 1955 Pan American Games, comparable to a regional Olympics, were held at the university.

In designing the stadium the engineers noted that everyone likes to sit near the 50-yard line, so they created a structure that is low at each end and has a high sweep along each side. This puts more than the customary number of spectators in the most desirable zone. Seating is in two tiers, with a capacity of 103,000.

The stadium was shaped by scooping out soil and lava rock from the middle and using this material to build embankments along the sides. Not only did this method cut ordinary construction costs by more than half, but it provided a desired craterlike resemblance to Mexico's volcanoes. Very little steel or concrete was required except for facing the compacted dirt fills and for the cantilevered balcony and the 48 access ramps and tunnels.

The stadium has a complete floodlighting system, a public-addresss system that reaches all areas, a 200-foot-long press box and outlets for television cameras at strategic points in addition to telephone, telegraph and teletypewriter facilities.

On another part of the campus are an eight-lane Olympic championship swimming pool, a huge practice pool and a championship diving pool. All three pools are connected by water channels spanned by low bridges. Casual swimmers can wander from pool to pool.

The water is heated, chemically purified and automatically circulated. The championship diving and swimming pools have underwater lighting and underwater windows from which the coaches can watch the form displayed by their students. Spectators were seated on a few rows of stone steps when the pools were first used. After the first big water meet was held it was found necessary to add a spectator stand.

Other sports facilities on the campus include a baseball stadium with seats for 3000 spectators, a practice stadium for field and track with bleachers seating 4000 people, three practice fields for soccer or American football, and an indoor court for the fast Latin-American game of jai alai.

Also on the campus are two softball diamonds, a dozen tennis courts, a dozen outdoor basketball courts that also are suitable for volleyball, eight courts for the game called handball fronton, and eight larger courts for a Latin-American game similar to squash. The exterior walls of these courts are sloped like Mexico's ancient pyramids and are faced with rough volcanic stone taken from the site.

Academic buildings on the campus are arranged in groups. Some are large enough to contain all the facilities for such subjects as dentistry or chemistry. This arrangement allows a student of dentistry, for example, to go from class to class without rushing from one part of the huge campus to another. Some of the classroom buildings are glass-walled skyscrapers, others are long and low, and still others rest on platforms that are supported above the ground on concrete pillars.

Near the Pavilion of Cosmic Rays is the Institute of Nuclear Physics with an adjoining "Garden of Radiation" surrounded by stone walls to absorb the rays from atom-smashing machines.

One outstanding building is the central library. From a distance it looks like a huge, oblong, intricately decorated cake. The structure is 116 feet tall, 190 feet long and 45 feet wide, and each of its exterior walls is ornamented with mosaic murals depicting stages in Mexico's history. Each mosaic consists of millions of bits of rock ranging from black obsidian to brown and pink marbles painstakingly cemented in place.

The two lower floors of the library contain reading rooms with windows of thin, translucent sheets of white marble. The 10 upper floors of the structure have no windows and contain storage stacks with a capacity of 120,000 volumes in addition to microfilm files.

Mexico is a center of mural art, and murals of various kinds are used for ornamenting large areas on many of the buildings. Some murals are painted in vivid plastic paints and others are composed of small glass tiles that were fired especially for the university. Still others, as in the case of Diego Rivera's ornamentation on the stadium walls, are made up of stones cut to shape and stained to the desired colors by means of acids.

It was a happy coincidence when Mexico decided to erect its new center of knowledge on the Pedregal. More than 80 centuries ago a strong civilization flourished there. Then a succession of lava flows from a near-by volcano buried all evidence of human existence except one pyramidlike temple that still projects up through the volcanic rock. Known as Cuicuilco, this temple is judged to be the oldest thing built by man that exists on the American continent. On the site of this ancient civilization now stands the newest campus in the world.

The sprawling campus was designed by 150 architects, built by 10,000 workers and provides facilities for 28,000 students. "University City," was started in 1950, cost Mexico $50,000,000

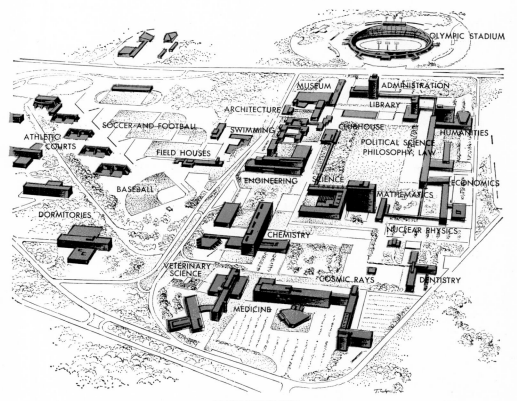

Four Major Approaches to the Control of Fusion

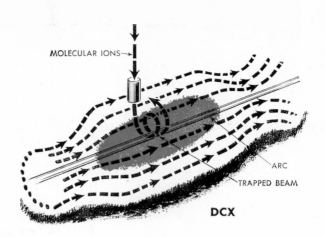

MOLECULAR IONS

ARC

TRAPPED BEAM

DCX

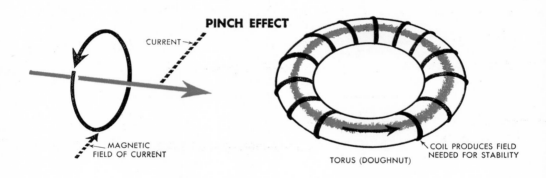

PINCH EFFECT

CURRENT

MAGNETIC FIELD OF CURRENT

COIL PRODUCES FIELD NEEDED FOR STABILITY

TORUS (DOUGHNUT)

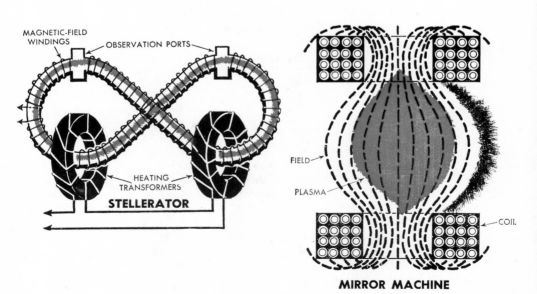

MAGNETIC-FIELD WINDINGS

OBSERVATION PORTS

HEATING TRANSFORMERS

STELLERATOR

FIELD

PLASMA

COIL

MIRROR MACHINE

In the Scylla instrument, a bank of capacitors sends tremendous discharge to tube

The Coming of Fusion Power

Scientists are knocking down the last barriers around the control of fusion reactions. Soon fusion will provide the world with inexpensive power

by Clifford B. Hicks

The scene was straight from a grade-B horror movie. Scientists at control panels pushed buttons and threw switches to create blinding bolts of lightning in a weird array of glowing vacuum tubes.

This was no horror movie, though. It was the Atoms for Peace exhibit of the 1958 Geneva Conference. The visitor could pause to inspect machines with such out-of-this-world names as Stellerator, Scylla, Astron, Alpha, Ogra, Zeta and the mildly optimistic Perhapsatron. The significance of this equipment—and the guarded optimism at the conference—was inescapable.

All over the world, scientists are making big strides in their efforts to harness for peaceful ends the fury of the H-bomb.

Indeed, as the visitor paused before the machines in the exhibit hall, he may well have been witnessing nuclear fusion. Some of the scientists have a sneaking suspicion that at least one of the instruments actually was producing fusion energy during the time it was on display.

The best evidence of progress in this field is not success, but lack of failure. As former Atomic Energy Commission Chairman Lewis L. Strauss has pointed out: "We think the fact that we have worked with it now for a number of years and have not been able to prove it impossible is a very considerable gauge of its eventual success."

Dr. Arthur E. Ruark, chief of controlled nuclear research for the AEC, confirms the optimism: "There is general belief in the American laboratories that the ignition temperature [the temperature at which the fusion reaction is self-sustaining] will be achieved within a few years."

Proof of success will be the discovery of invisible particles which the scientists wryly call "thermonukes" (thermonuclear neutrons). All over the world, right now, scientists are seeking thermonukes. It's a baffling search because a thermonuke is exactly like any other neutron, so how do you prove the origin of the little beast?

Whether thermonukes attended the Geneva Conference or not, scientists in attendance estimated that sometime within the next 10 to 20 years a switch will be thrown and the first full-scale, power-producing fusion reactor will go into operation. Even this first crude reactor probably will have a power output comparable to the huge hydroelectric plant at Hoover Dam.

That moment, if it comes, will be a pivot point of history. Nations need never fear that their power sources will run dry. For a time, obviously, petroleum will remain as a source of mobile power, and coal will continue to provide industry with heat. You can't change a way of life overnight. But eventually, according to the experts, oil will give way to some form of stored electrical power which has been derived from the fusion reaction, and coal will be simply another source of industrial chemicals.

At that supreme moment, man can look ahead through the halls of time for literally billions of years and still see a plentiful supply of fuel. *Billions of years!* When new kilowatts are needed, they simply will be plucked from sea water.

Why will fusion reactors be so much better than today's fission reactors?

1. The fuel supply, as noted above, will be inexhaustible and inexpensive.

2. The problem of disposing of radioactive wastes will be negligible. This is a major problem of fission reactors. The critters are just plain dirty. For example, if all our current energy requirements were provided by fission reactors, we'd have to dispose of radioactive waste material equivalent to that from the explosion of 200,000 atomic bombs *each year.* Fusion reactors will produce very little radioactive waste.

3. The fusion reaction, by its nature, is safer than fission. A fusion reactor could never explode. It would simply collapse and fail to function.

4. There's a fascinating possibility that electricity can be drawn directly out of a fusion reactor. In fission, the reactor produces heat, which then is pumped through conventional turbines and generators to produce electricity. This is a highly inefficient way of producing electricity from nuclear energy.

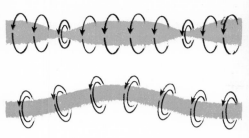

Right, a circular tube is used in studies of the pinch effect. An electrical field squeezes high-temperature gas into thin "rope." The big problem with this method is that the "rope" tends to break

To achieve fusion, the scientist must crack the secrets of those stars, for nuclear fusion has been generating sunshine and starlight since the beginning of time. It is really the basic source of power of the universe. In effect, the scientists must create a star on earth, bottle it up and clamp on a lid. If he succeeds, he can draw from the bottle any amount of power he wishes.

But each step in this field is a tremendous effort. Dr. Amasa S. Bishop, in a recent AEC report on fusion research, stated that progress may be "slow and halting" because of the many problems involved, but that as yet "no basic obstacle" has been uncovered.

Just what are the obstacles, basic or otherwise? Only a top physicist can understand the mathematics of the fusion process, but the basic idea isn't difficult to comprehend. Suppose you want to bottle up your own star. Here's how you'd go about it:

First, you might be wise to review the differences between fission (A-bomb energy) and fusion (H-bomb energy). In a fission reactor, the nuclei or "cores" of atoms are broken apart. The process has been compared to the explosion of ordinary TNT. Touch off TNT with a blasting cap, and the shock explodes one molecule, which explodes the next, etc., in a chain reaction. Similarly in a fission reactor, atoms are blasted into particles, which blast other atoms into particles, etc. Poof! You either have an A-bomb explosion or controlled fission, depending upon the speed of the process. In either case you get a scad of atomic particles and considerable energy.

In a fusion reaction, however, these atomic "cores" are forced, against their wishes, to unite. This process is somewhat similar to the burning of logs in your fireplace. You give the molecules of the logs a hotfoot by burning kindling under them. They become so agitated they collide violently, forcing them to unite, and the logs burst into flame. Once the logs are ablaze, the fire itself continues to heat the molecules, so the reaction is self-sustaining. Similarly, in a fusion reactor you raise the temperature to force nuclei to unite. Only in the case of nuclear fusion, you must give the nuclei a superhotfoot, raising the temperature to hundreds of millions of degrees. You must create the temperature of the stars.

For a moment, forget about the problem of kindling such a fire, and concentrate upon the fuel itself. Where **do you get atomic "cores"** suitable for the fusion process? The most promising source is deuterium, which is simply one form of hydrogen. Turn on the faucet at the kitchen sink, and you'll let an untold quantity of deuterium flow down the drain. Deuterium is found in ordinary water everywhere.

You might suspect that there is a hitch here, that it would be expensive to extract deuterium from water. The United States already is producing deuterium on a significant scale, and published figures indicate that it can be extracted so cheaply that deuterium as a fuel would cost about one percent as much as coal!

Now assume that you have extracted just two of these deuterium nuclei, which are called deuterons. If you can hurl these two deuterons at each other with enough force to make them fuse, you will create three things: helium atoms, neutrons—and from 3.25 to 4 million electron volts, an incredible amount of energy. Here is an example of just how much energy: If you "burn" or fuse just *one pound* of these deuterons, you'll end up with *43 million kilowatt-hours* of electricity, the equivalent in energy of more than a million gallons of gasoline!

If all the deuterium in the world were extracted from the sea and burned completely, it would produce one thousand million, million, million kilowatt-*years* of electricity, a figure beyond comprehension. To put it in a much more credible way, just 10 gallons of ordinary tap water contain enough deuterium to supply all the electrical requirements of your family for one full year. And this much fuel, even now, can be separated from the water for less than 30 cents!

Such are the stakes in this scientific game.

How do you go about fusing deuterons? Each deuteron has a positive electrical charge, so they repel each other with incredible violence. Whenever two deuterons approach, they instantly fly apart. The only way to force them together is to heat them. Then, like ants on a hot stove, they'll move so fast they'll collide blindly before they have a chance to recognize each other.

The temperature of the "stove" must be a hundred million degrees or more. At that temperature, atoms break down into free electrons and nuclei. This gaseous mixture is called a *plasma*. The electrons in the plasma will be traveling 90,000 miles per second, and the deuterons at 1500 miles per second. This is precisely what is happening in the stars of the sky.

Obviously, finding a bottle to hold a star is the toughest obstacle science has ever tackled. The melting point of the most heat-resistant of known solids is around 3000 degrees. Strange as it sounds, however, heat is not much of a problem, as there is very little actual heat in

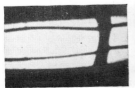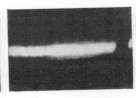

This series of photographs shows the gas being squeezed into a thin "rope"

the bottle. The plasma is such a thin gas that, although individual particles are superhot, the total heat content is not very high. In fact, even when a liter of the gas reaches 350 million degrees it will hold just about enough heat to make a cup of coffee palatable!

The big problem, from the standpoint of the physicist, is *keeping* the gas hot. If the deuterons, in their wild dance, should touch the sides of the bottle, the gas would instantly be cooled to a point where fusion couldn't take place.

Since the ants on this hot griddle all have an electrical charge, they should be subject to control in a magnetic field. This is the approach that is being tried on a worldwide basis in the search for the elusive thermonukes. Anyone investigating this field is somewhat surprised to discover that there are virtually no security wraps on the research in magnetic bottles. Research papers show that scientists apparently are approaching the last difficult steps to success. Significant numbers of neutrons have been captured in some of the equipment. Whether they are true thermonukes, or neutrons from side reactions, has not yet been proved.

So far, four different approaches to the magnetic bottle have been tried:

1. The first method takes advantage of the so-called "pinch effect." In this method, a strong magnetic field is created around the plasma, forcing it away from the sides of the bottle and into a sort of rope. As the current is increased, the rope tends to shrink, constricting or pinching the deuterons into a narrow field where the temperature builds up and they are more likely to collide. This is the technique used in the famous Zeta machine of the British. The principal difficulty is that the plasma rope begins to writhe, creating such kinks and "sausage links" that it destroys itself. As Dr. Ruark says, "Asking the pinched current to stay quietly in the middle of the tube is something like asking a boa constrictor not to constrict." Still, ways are being found to tame the boa. One is to place a strong magnetic field down the middle of the plasma, giving it a sort of spine or stiffener.

2. A more recent approach, under investigation at the University of California Radiation Laboratory, is a "magnetic mirror." This instrument consists of a long straight tube surrounded by coils of wire to create a field around the plasma, preventing it from reaching the sides of the tube. At each end of the tube, extra strong magnetic fields or "mirrors" reflect stray particles back, holding the plasma in an unbelievably hot ball. This creates a more stable plasma, but there is one disadvantage: Before this reaction will be self-sustaining, it may be necessary to raise the temperature of the plasma to a billion degrees or more.

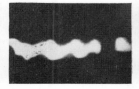

Then the kinks begin to form and within microseconds "rope" distintegrates

3. One of the most promising approaches is the Stellerator at Princeton. In this technique, the tube is either doughnut-shaped or formed into a figure 8. After the plasma has been heated to about a million degrees, the deuterons are further speeded by alternating the field rapidly (called magnetic pumping).

4. An apparatus called DCX at Oak Ridge National Laboratory is basically a new means of injecting deuterium into the magnetic bottle. The deuterium atoms are shot into a static magnetic field, where a carbon arc blasts them into electrons and nuclei. This creates a very high temperature plasma from the outset, and the system, if successful, should be useful in the Stellerator and some of the other instruments.

Scientists, who normally are cautious men, tend to be surprisingly optimistic about one or more of these approaches. An AEC brochure at the Geneva exhibit, for example, states that when Stellerator C is completed in 1960, "it is expected to be capable of producing abundant thermonuclear fusion reactions."

Even if reactions are achieved, there is no guarantee that a true power-producing reactor is possible. But the stakes are so high in this game that most countries are boosting their ante each year. Since 1953 the AEC funds for fusion research have increased 1000 percent.

The best part of this game is that if one player wins, all win. It seems quite likely that within the next year, scientists at a laboratory somewhere on the face of the earth, will capture significant quantities of genuine thermonukes. And in 10 to 20 years, the first successful fusion reactor will go into operation.

Such a tremendous stride will herald the day when bottled stars will glow everywhere, and every man will have an incredible amount of power at his fingertips.

The novel shape of the pretzel-type Stellerator helps prevent kinks from forming, concentrates plasma in the "magnetic bottle"

Parts of the road had been swept away and had to be rebuilt

ADVENTURE on the STILWELL ROAD

Six English youths visited the wartime trail made famous by General Stilwell and found that it has been swallowed up by the jungle

By Adrian Cowells

We left "Hellgate," the last Indian post, climbed the 4000 muddy feet of gloomy mountainside and there, poised in Pangsu Pass, we and our escort halted in the rain and made a last brew of coffee.

We were six graduates from Oxford and Cambridge, though with our beards, rainproof jackets and jungle boots there was little to connect us with an English university except the signs on our car doors. They read: "The Oxford and Cambridge Far Eastern Expedition." We had left England five months before and motored across Europe, the Middle East and India to our base camp at Assam. Singapore was our

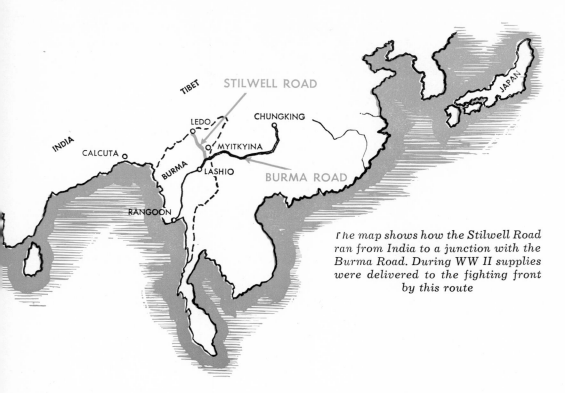

The map shows how the Stilwell Road ran from India to a junction with the Burma Road. During WW II supplies were delivered to the fighting front by this route

goal. We were trying to find an overland route across the span of Eurasia from London to Singapore.

Burma was the big obstacle, the one which had stopped everyone else. People said it was impossible; that the two wartime routes (the Stilwell and Imphal Roads) had been won for only a short period from the mud mires and craggy ranges of one of the world's most vicious jungle areas; that the roads had decayed under 10 years of encroaching jungle and monsoon rainfall.

But we were not convinced. The Burmese government had given us overland visas, though they were granted "at your own risk." We had managed to get information on bandit positions. It might be true that no one knew anything about the routes into Burma, but we felt there was no harm in finding out for ourselves.

We had tents, camping gear and food to last more than a month; petrol tanks which would take us 1000 miles; power winches to pull the cars up a cliff or out of a river; equipment to build bridges; and two of the toughest four-wheel-drive, 10-gear vehicles in the world, our Landrovers.

And so, as we drank our coffee at the top of the pass, our escort told us what little was known of the road, and we told them what we had learned from conversations with former soldiers and engineers who, years before, had helped build it.

A week after Pearl Harbor the Japanese had invaded Burma and in a lightning campaign seized the Burma Road, drove a wedge between India and China and cut off Chiang Kai-shek from his supply line to America.

Some of the defeated British, Chinese and American forces in the north jettisoned their vehicles and retreated through the tangled morass of marsh and jungle which stretched between Myitkyina and India, staggered over the Patkai Hills into Hellgate. They had established the trail which was to become the Stilwell Road, but at that time men called it the "Road of Death."

One of the survivors was Lt. Gen. Joseph Stilwell. "I claim we got an awful beating," he said. "We got run out of Burma. I think we ought to go back and retake it." An army of millions of men under his charge was helpless until the supply line was established again.

To open the route he planned to blast a highway and oil pipeline from Assam to the old Burma Road. As an engineering project, to be carried out in the face of two Japanese divisions, it seemed fantastic. And because one man forced it into creation it was named in his honor —the Stilwell Road.

The road was built by 10 engineer battalions behind a screen of jungle fighters. In that evil land, 200 inches of rain poured down each year, rivers rose 30 feet in a day. When Lord Louis Mountbatten flew over the route, he asked someone the name of the river below. "That's no river," said an American looking down at the sheet of water. "That's Stilwell's road." "Vinegar Joe" himself described it as "Rain, rain, rain, mud, mud, mud, typhus, malaria, dysentery, exhaustion, rotting feet, body sores."

In the mountains, landslides washed bulldozers into 1000-foot jungle chasms. A mule once sank right out of sight in the mud.

But the macadam moved inevitably forward. Men of all races, speaking 200 different dialects, struggled ahead thigh-deep in the mud. At a mile a day the road advanced. To build it, the Allies created the longest line of communication of the war—12,000 miles across two oceans, by pipe, rail or river steamer to Assam—and—when the highway was finally finished—by 1079 miles of jungle and mountain to Kunming.

To operate that thin macadam strip, 360,000 square miles had to be conquered at a great loss of human life.

On January 27, 1945, the eastbound armies met those from China and the road was through. Seven months later, atomic smoke mush-roomed upward above Hiroshima, heralding the end of the war. From that day the Stilwell Road has been forgotten, decaying into the jungle.

This was the ghost we had come to find.

We set out in silence as our escort bade farewell. The road was gone. What was left was a thinning undergrowth and stone foundations under the mud, mud which lined the track like grease on a garage floor. Our cars slithered between the narrow jungle walls. The track twisted and turned, clinging to the impossible contours of the mountainside, never straight for more than 30 yards. Occasionally we could see, 1000 feet below, the surly green of the jungle in a valley.

Soon we realized that our main problem was the streams of that mountainside. Some of the bridges were down, wood yellow with rot, decaying into the water. Sometimes a Landrover stuck in the river bed, and water dashed in one door and out the other as we waded with winch and cable. Sometimes we came to an old Bailey bridge and laid logs across it to provide a surface. On occasion a whole span would sag under us.

Members of the expedition pose with the equipment they carried over "Vinegar Joe's" road. It includes bridge-building equipment and food for a month

But despite it all we descended by the second day into the bowl of the Upper Chindwin. That was our tribute to a great engineering feat: A road so well built that after years of neglect in that impossible environment it still survived. Naturally the macadam was gone, scrub encroaching, bridges swept away. But there was nothing which six men and Landrovers with power winches couldn't overcome.

As we came down into the valley we left the land of the Nagas (their last head-hunting war had been in 1952). We had been warned about them, but the few we saw were timid, small, cheerful and carried nothing but knives. Most of the other forest men had homemade muzzle-loading muskets or wartime rifles loaded with ammunition dated 1942. But none of them could have been more friendly.

All the way down the road we had been passing the ruins of war. We picked up a torn helmet from the upturned cab of a lorry. We poked inside a tank for snakes, and tried to identify the remains of enormous construction machines. There were stacks of oil drums, mounds of corrugated iron, skeletons of Jeeps and bulldozers. "Did you find any human skeletons?" is a question we are frequently asked. No, not a sign.

We traveled down the red dirt until we crossed the river at Tanai, where we met our first representative of the Burmese government, a local district official in a *lungyi* (sarong). He concealed his surprise and refused to do anything so rude as to ask for our passports. "Would you like a game of badminton?" was all he had said. We later learned from him that there was practically no traffic on the higher part of the road, though six trucks a year moved short distances between villages. He was surprised that it was possible to come from India.

We drove on next day through a forest valley, then passed Walawbum,

Shaduzup and Kamaing—names attached to nothing but a dozen huts in a jungle clearing and a memory of heavily fought battles. Then the valley disappeared and we entered Myitkyina, past the great airstrip which had been seized by Merrill's Marauders in one of the most successful jungle surprises of the war.

"Boy, oh boy! I sure am glad to see you!" were the first words we heard as we climbed out of the cars. A tall, smiling man came forward to pump our hands. "I sort of got left by the war," he said, and pointed at his "business," a wooden hut with mechanic's tools outside and, at a guess, a Burmese wife inside.

In fact, most things in that part of Burma have been leftover by the war. Huts were made of upturned trucks, knives ground from car springs, and money earned by banditry with a wartime rifle. Transport was almost entirely by one of the 15,000 Jeeps and trucks the American army is said to have left behind, and I once saw a woman wearing Japanese epaulets hanging like rings from her ears.

We left Myitkyina by a ferry constructed of two Bailey pontoons lashed together and powered by a homemade adaptation of a car engine. On the pontoon ferry was a lorry, in the lorry the band of some Kachin troops who refused to cross until they had played for us. Nine men with bamboo pipes, a drummer and a wild-eyed character who rhythmically beat a jungle knife against the lorry's metal side produced a weird, whimsical melody; all the more whimsical when we realized the tunes were Orientalized renderings of "Swanee River" and "Home Sweet Home," obviously picked up from U.S. troops. They smiled at our camera. They grinned bashfully at our tape recorder. They roared at their sergeant when he ordered them to move. They laughed at everything.

From there we began the mountain climb toward the junction with the Burma Road. It was a dramatic journey. The road climbed and turned like an Alpine racecourse, but instead of macadam there were

After 10 years, this bridge was covered with vegetation

dust and cobbles. We saw a few Jeeps and lorries on the road, the only vehicles that could manage it.

One morning we stopped at a village market while a couple of men worked on the Landrovers. All manner of natives dressed in all kinds of costumes gaped at us. "Strange-looking Charlies," remarked one of our mechanics as he wiped a black hand across a dusty face, filthy shirt dangling over shaggy shorts, unbathed for a fortnight, the whole apparition crowned by a tufted beard and a disintegrating straw hat. I wonder what the natives were saying.

As we journeyed we found that, because of our black beards, we were frequently taken for Italian missionaries. We quickly corrected the mistake. A missionary had been shot by bandits only a month before.

One night our camp was a quarter mile from the Chinese border and we could see on the other side what we later learned was the "Flying Tigers'" last airbase. Two of our men poled across the frontier river in a bamboo raft to have a look, landed in China, exchanged a few words with a passing peasant and returned to be "brainwashed" by the rest of us.

Finally one morning our dirt track came to a crossing, and the other road was made of macadam. We had come to the Burma Road, and the end of Stilwell's impossible engineering feat. On a signpost: Kunming 606 miles.

We had started our journey on the Stilwell Road partially to rediscover a wartime campaign. Instead, we had found a smiling, delightful people. The tragedy we had expected lay not in the decay of the road, but in the impact of the war on a primitive people.

In a way, we were glad the highway had become a forgotten one.

The explorers pose in a Japanese tank, one of many war remnants they ran across

This electronic device "Audrey," reacts intelligently to 10 spoken numbers

Tantalizing Telephones

Americans like to talk. Each day they make 228 million telephone calls — more than half of the world's total. We gabby folk are pushing the communications experts to speedier and more efficient service. Here's what they have planned

By Richard F. Dempewolff

Reaching across the kitchen counter, a housewife presses a button on a streamlined gadget resembling a miniature radio. "One, one—five—seven, five, eight, oh," she says to a built-in microphone. On a two-inch-square screen in the face of the instrument, light glows and the image of a man appears. "Darling," says the housewife, "stop off on the way home and pick up a pie." The face on the screen grins. A voice comes from the miniature loudspeaker, "Sure thing, honey. Be home in half an hour."

A peek into the distant future? Not so distant as you think. Bell Laboratories' director of apparatus development, Robert Nossaman,

Left, by turning knob on Dialaphone to the name of a person, the call is automatically made. Below, telephone has built-in alarm clock

thinks a production-model TV phone may be available to any subscriber within 15 years. Last year Nossaman's boys built an experimental model, with a switch that cuts off the picture if you're answering from the shower, or want privacy for any reason.

Already, a loudspeaker-telephone for use on regular customer service has gone into production in Sweden. Known as the WeGe-Phone, the instrument has microphone and speaker built into a single unit. Conversations can be held between two or more people, as though chatting in the same room. For privacy, a built-in handset can be detached for use. Most prophetic feature, however, is the tiny loudspeaker opening designed for a future miniature TV tube. A similar phone, developed by Stromberg Carlson, was marketed in this country last year. It resembles a standard desk set, with separate mike.

One hurdle to practical TV-phones is the amount of electronic information necessary for transmitting voice and picture over existing telephone lines. Now that may be licked. Last winter, General Electric scientists announced a "slow-scan TV," which can be sent out over conventional telephone wires. Instead of transmitting 30 complete pictures every second as commercial TV does, slow-scan sends a new image only once in five or ten seconds. The party on the other end might jump around on your telephone screen, but he'd come in loud and clear.

Actually, scientists at Bell Telephone Laboratories' research plant in New Jersey admit they have all the necessary hardware and know-how to produce TV telephones right now. But they doubt that many subscribers would want to pay "several dozen dollars" for a three-minute call just to see the expression on somebody's face across town. Even when the cost factor is solved, nobody is sure residential subscribers will go for an extra fee just to peer at each other remotely. But telephone officials do believe they'll soon be making TV telephones for special business applications. A magazine make-up man, for instance, could flash his pages on the TV-phone screen while he talked with the

Left, buzzing device tells when phone call is being held. Below experimental TV-phone

printer about corrections. Maps, architectural renderings, blueprints and such will be television-phoned anyplace, eliminating time-consuming verbal description. Right now, a closed-circuit telephone-television system is in operation for rapid confirmation of reservations in New York's Pennsylvania Railroad Station. Many banks have installed Data Vision, a similar system, that permits tellers to check account balances and signatures in central files, miles from the teller's cage.

One major frustration about to bite the dust is the "busy signal." New automatic electronic-telephone exchanges already are eliminating this nuisance. In Sweden, if you dial a number through the new L. M. Ericsson exchange, it's no longer necessary to "try again" if the number you want is busy. Just hang up and forget it. The exchange's brain "memorizes" your call, stacks it with any others that might be waiting for the same number, then rings back each caller on a "first come, first served" basis as the line clears. In England, a similar exchange developed by Pye Telecommunications does the same job noiselessly, using electronic "valves" instead of switches. Since there are no moving contacts, the exchange is great for mines or explosive atmosphere. No dustfree air-conditioned rooms are necessary.

Within the next couple of years, an experimental electronic exchange will do the same things for 3000 customers in Morris, Ill., marking the start of a gradual change to electronic switching throughout this country.

Some of the new electronic-telephone genii are so uncanny people don't have to do any talking at all—transistors and tubes do it for them. Right now, the Automatic Electric Company of Northlake, Ill., can provide you with an electronic telephone watchdog to guard your property. Dubbed the "electronic sentry," this shoe-box-size robot will put in a call to the proper people whenever it senses trouble due to fire, thievery, atmospheric pressures, temperature, water levels in tanks, boilers and such. The little unit gets its information from thermostats, pressure gauges, burglar detectors and any other control you choose to hook it up to. Whenever its sensitive brain is "frightened" by one of these sensory gadgets, the sentry automatically connects itself across the telephone line, dials the proper authority—police, firemen, plumber or whoever's needed—selects the right message from a bank of tapes and transmits a recorded warning until help comes.

If the robot "watchdog" doesn't raise your goose pimples, American Telephone and Telegraph may do it with their Dataphone, recently perfected at Bell Labs. This telephonic device enables business machines to "talk" to each other at a rate of 1000 words a minute. The Dataphone takes impulses from a data-processing brain and turns them into tones on a magnetic tape. The tones are transmitted over telephone lines. At the other end, another device switches the tones back to impulses and feeds them into business machines that can print the information on paper. A.T.&T. president, Frederick Kappel, reveals that his Dataphone robot can deliver 7000 supermarket inventory items in 16 minutes, for instance, or process and transmit a similar quantity of payroll data to a field force.

Pushing the communications experts to constantly speedier and more efficient service are chatty Americans who now place 228,000,000 calls from some 65,000,000 telephones every day (more than half the world's total of 111,500,000). In another 20 years, the experts expect those figures will double. Even with high-speed electronic exchanges, present transmission facilities could never carry the load. So, while line crews are busy building radio relays and stringing thousands of miles of wire and coaxial cable each year, the laboratory wizards are taxing their ingenuity to find new ways of crowding those channels. According to Dr. Claud Shannon at Bell Labs, an ordinary telephone wire can carry some 28,000 tiny "bits" of information each second, but an average spoken message only conveys 40 bits per second. So Shannon is trying to squeeze conversation into solid lumps for transmission.

One upshot of this is a piece of electronic magic called a "vocoder." While you talk, this incredible robot turns your voice into a series of

Extra buttons allow the setting up of conference calls between remote and local stations

hoots, whistles and beeps that shoot over the lines in record time. At the other end, the sizzling cacophony is converted back to words. The device enables 10 times more data to be sent over one wire. The rub is that no human voice ever sounded like the vocoder, whose electronic vocal chords make everything come out sounding like 33⅓ played in 78 time on a 1915 phonograph.

To keep up with the gabby public, even the familiar old table-set phone is destined for a face lifting soon. One current phone item skidding into obsolescence is the dial. The new electronic switching systems can handle 100 digits per second. The lumbering dial takes 12 seconds to transmit seven digits, so it's a hindrance. Consequently, sometime in the next 10 years, when long-distance dialing allows you to sit in your home and dial direct to a friend in almost any major city, you probably won't actually "dial" him. Bell Laboratory scientists have perfected one device for the job called the "polytonic coder." You'll simply punch out the combination on 10 numbered buttons without lifting the receiver. This done, you'll lift the receiver and find your friend's phone already ringing. Another gadget, working on similar principles, uses a barrel-shaped affair, like the odometer on your car, at the phone's base. You set up the number you want just as you'd spin the mileage on an odometer, lift the receiver—and there's your party. Most fantastic of all, however, is Bell Laboratories' Audrey. An offspring of Vocoder, Bell's mechanical talking robot, Audrey is a panel of tubes and condensers that will "dial" a number for you when you have *spoken* it into the phone. "We've got her to the point where she can be adjusted to recognize any one person," says an A.T.&T. official. "She'll even dial a number spoken in a Scotsman's brogue."

Another number-getter designed to save manicured fingernails is the Dialaphone, a sort of combination phone book and robot dialer already being produced by James Kilburg Corporation in San Mateo, Calif. It's about the size and shape of a desk-top "squawk box." To operate it, the caller turns a small handle until the name of the party

Above, Swedish phone has loudspeaker alongside dial for handless and group telephoning. Right, movement of coin tells caller how much time remains

he wants shows up in a slot window. Then he pushes a button, the gremlins go to work, and when he picks up his phone the party he wants is on the line. The Dialaphone's private gremlin is a memory tape, prepunched with several hundred frequently called numbers, in code. As a name appears in the window, the perforations designating the phone number for that person fall in place on a decoder that transmits the number to the exchange in a fraction of a second. "If you can think of a man's name, you don't need to remember his number," says Kilburg. "And the Dialaphone never dials a wrong number."

The new coast-to-coast dialing poses an interesting stickler—the national directory, which would be a classic volume about 10 feet thick. Hence, several ingenious solutions are already in the works. Graphic Microfilm of New England has come up with the idea for a boxlike affair not much larger than a big-city directory. Numbers for the entire network, stored on microfilm inside the box, can be brought into position and projected on a screen by simply flipping a lever.

The hard fact is that many of "tomorrow's" telephonic fantasies exist today. Want to call Tokyo from an airplane flying 15,000 feet above Wisconsin? You can do it. Two Northwest Orient Airlines' planes have a phone in the passenger cabin for anyone aboard to place or receive calls. Right now the call must be made within 175 miles of Chicago or Detroit, where the two radiotelephone stations equipped to handle this traffic are located. Lights flash and a bell rings when there's a call for someone aboard.

You can count on seeing lots more radiotelephonics for everyone. Last year Stromberg Carlson introduced a miniature radio-telephone receiver about the size of an electric razor. Anybody can buy one. It fits in vest pocket or handbag. If you're out shopping or strolling the streets within eight miles of home or office, and there's a phone call for you, the tiny transistor radio will start buzzing. Just head for the nearest pay phone, dial a prearranged number and you'll be piped in to the call. How does it work? In the cities where the service is available, a special operator intercepts all calls to your telephone when a flipped switch on the instrument tells her you're going out. On a compact transmitter resembling an adding machine, she broadcasts the signal that tickles your radio buzzer wherever you are. Then she patches you in to the caller when you dial in.

In the Hamburg, Germany, railroad station, when you drop your coins for a long-distance call, they slide into a long sloping slot; callers can gauge how much talk time is left by watching the coins drop away.

A new kind of phone box is already appearing on American street corners. Strapped to lamp posts, the brightly painted aluminum cases contain outdoor telephone sets with direct connection to police or fire departments. When the handset is lifted, a light flashes on a console at headquarters—no dialing necessary. The emergency is immediately reported, and the man at the console knows where it's from by the position of the light.

If all this is here, what's in store for the future? At Massachusetts Institute of Technology, Dr. W. N. Locke is busy working on an electronic translator of the printed word. When a current study of language sounds is finished, Dr. Locke believes that an electronic device can be built that will automatically translate foreign languages.

The mountain in the background consists of millions of tons of gold-free rock

Mountains of Gold and Uranium

Africa, the world's leading producer of gold, mines it and uranium in one operation

By Peter Holz

The quest for gold has been one of the great driving forces of mankind for centuries. Interest in gold—that highly prized and most readily exchangeable commodity—was fanned in the 19th century by the great gold rushes of California, the Yukon, Australia and finally South Africa. The discovery of gold on the Witwatersrand—the Ridge of White Water in the mineral-saturated Transvaal—was the glorious climax to all these discoveries. Today, South Africa is still the world's leading producer of the yellow metal.

Fifty-four mines, stretching in a golden arc of roughly 300 miles from the Transvaal to the arid Orange Free State produce 54 percent of the total world production of gold. From these mines, gold travels to practically every country in the world to fulfill its vital function of standing security behind paper money, and of helping the flow of international commerce.

South Africa is rich in many minerals. Asbestos, chrome, manganese, copper, platinum, tungsten, tin and lead are all mined there. But gold, and lately, uranium, are the important money producers. Some 15,373,680 ounces of gold were produced in 1956, representing a value of $548,840,375. The mines have certainly come a long way since the '80s, when pioneers from the four corners of the world, including of course the United States, flocked to South Africa to stake their claim in the newly discovered El Dorado. Today 50,000 Europeans and almost seven times that number of Africans are employed in gold-mining operations in the fabulous "golden arc."

Some of the mines are almost 10,000 feet deep. Three of the largest of the Union of South Africa's mining-finance companies are at present cooperating in a new mine, where gold-bearing ore will be brought up from a depth of more than two miles. Planning for this project, which when completed will have cost $60,000,000, has been going on for the past 15 years. Because of the high temperature at 12,500 feet, a ventilation system capable of pumping 1,500,000 cubic feet of air per minute down the main shafts will be installed. By the time this mine has "died" in about 60 years, it will have produced $2,400,000,000 worth of gold.

Characteristic of every mine are the tall headgears, the older ones constructed of riveted-steel sections and plates, the more recent ones built of reinforced concrete. Just as familiar to South Africans are the

Here miners prepare to blast a tunnel through the mineral-rich rock

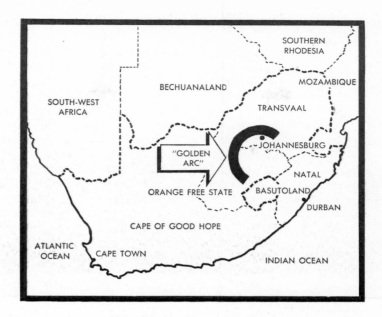

pale-yellow mine dumps which adjoin every mining property. They build up over the years and consist of millions of tons of crushed rock from which the gold has been wrested. Attempts have been made in the past to cover these eyesores with trees and grass, but with little success. The barren sand, saturated with cyanide, is poor soil for vegetation. It has also been suggested that worked-out shafts and tunnels be filled with the yellow sand, just to get rid of it, but the cost of doing so would be prohibitive.

Underground, the mines are minor cities with engine rooms, first-aid stations, repair shops and storerooms. There is unceasing activity down there. Men drill holes in the quartz, fill them with dynamite, blast, collect the broken rock and hoist it to the surface at roughly 30 miles per hour. About 67,500,000 tons are brought to the surface annually— enough material there for roughly 425 Empire State buildings!

On the surface the ore is collected in huge stockpiles and screened to separate the large from the small pieces of gold-bearing rock. The larger pieces are reduced in rock breakers, and much of the waste rock is picked out by hand at this stage by teams of Africans. For many of these Africans, working in a gold mine is their first clash with civilization. They flock to the mines from the bush to earn a little money. After a while they go back to their ancient way of life, telling their kinsmen of the inexplicable ways of the white man.

In the rows of ball mills, the rock is mixed with water and reduced to a fine pulp or slime. This is pumped to batteries of tanks containing a weak cyanide solution. The cyanide dissolves the gold and the solution is filtered in rotary filters. Following filtration, the gold-bearing solution is clarified, de-aerated and the gold finally precipitated. The resultant mud is fused with fluxing materials such as borax, and the gold cast into 1000-ounce bars. It is then sent to the world's largest gold refinery situated near Johannesburg. Each bar contains about 874 ounces of gold, 90 ounces of silver and 36 ounces of base metals. It

For many Africans, the mines are the first contact with the civilized world

leaves the refinery 99.6 percent pure gold, cast into bars weighing 400 ounces each. Each year, almost 38,500 such bars are produced.

It takes almost five tons of ore to produce one ounce of gold, roughly the size of a button.

In October 1952, South Africa's gold-mining industry began the extraction of uranium oxide. The work of extracting uranium oxide begins when gold has been extracted from the finely crushed ore by filtration. The residual goldfree slime is received in the uranium plants on conveyor belts and fed into tanks containing sulphuric acid. The solution is then filtered and the filtrate, containing the uranium oxide, subjected to a number of further processes until a pure uranium solution is obtained. Uranium oxide is precipitated as a bright-yellow mud, which is dried and exported to the United States and Great Britain for further purification and ultimate use in the nuclear industry.

Some years ago fears were expressed in mining circles that the gold mines, some of them more than 60 years old, would die one by one, leading ultimately to a great wave of depression. These fears appear to be without foundation, for as one mine is worked out and closed down, another new mining venture takes its place. After World War II, nine new mines were built in the Orange Free State.

In all mining operations there is a certain amount of uncertainty and an element of risk, and so it was with the new gold mines. While sinking the shafts, friable and fissured ground was encountered and sometimes water under terrific pressure would burst into the shafts at a rate of tens of thousands of gallons per hour. Diamond drills were subsequently used to penetrate in advance of shaft-sinking. As soon as water was struck, cement was injected at high pressure into the fissures to seal them.

By the end of 1957, millions of gallons of salty water had been pumped to the surface. Although the whole of the Orange Free State province suffers from a perpetual water shortage, both mines and the farming community were unable to make use of it because of its brackishness. It could not be pumped into the few existing rivers either, and means of disposing of it created a major problem. As natural evaporation can dispose of only about 4000 gallons per acre per day, some of the mines resorted to sprinkler systems to increase the evaporation process. Large evaporation dams dot the scene, but the solution as to what to do with the water lay in desalting it. Experiments were conducted on a huge scale until a satisfactory process was discovered. This process depends on the use of electric current which causes mineral impurities in the water to pass through so-called ion-selective membranes. These form the walls of cells through which the brackish water is pumped, thus reducing its mineral content. At present the world's first large-scale electrodialysis de-salting plant is under construction at a cost of $1,080,000.

South Africa is, of course, not the only country in Africa which mines gold. Ghana, Southern Rhodesia, the Belgian Congo and Tanganyika are all producers of the yellow metal. But it is in the Union of South Africa that the supply of gold seems almost inexhaustible, so with its gold and uranium sources, it has little to fear for its future, which promises to be as prosperous as its past.

Here gold is extracted from the slime, leaving uranium-rich waste

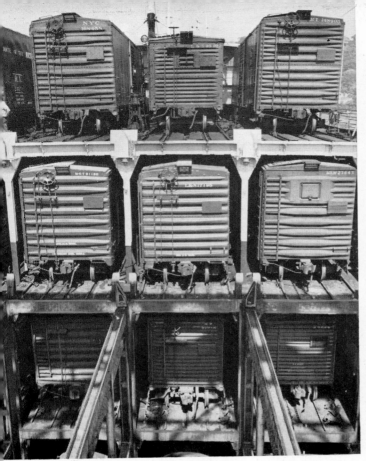

Cross-section of the Seatrain shows her decks loaded with freight cars

The Maritime Fleet

Our heavy-duty fleet moves everything from
orange juice to railroad cars
and looks pretty sleek while doing it

By Capt. W. D. Brinckloe, USN

In June 1942, the mechanized columns of Field Marshal Rommel's crack Afrika Corps ambushed the British Eighth Army in the Libyan Desert, smashing the greatest part of Montgomery's armor which stood between the Desert Fox and the road to Cairo. A month later a German U-boat caught a relief convoy south of Bermuda and ripped open the vitals of the freighters carrying the precious replacement tanks. Into the breach, with Rommel massing for the final drive and time running out, was thrust the seagoing train carrier SS *Seatrain Texas*. Her cavernous belly was crammed with tanks scraped by emergency Presidential order from American arsenals. Speed was her only pro-

At Edgewater, N. J., a giant crane lifts the freight cars from the ship's hold

Gets a Facelifting

tection against enemy wolf-packs. The coastwise car ship, built two years earlier to carry freight cars between New York and Texas, finished a harrowing 35-day trip around the Cape of Good Hope to Suez in time to throw her priceless cargo into a winning fight before El Alamein and become the heroine of the day.

The desert fighting is over (we hope), six ocean-going "carfloats" of Seatrain Lines are still busy. With the help of 125-ton cranes at various terminals these ships can disgorge 100 loaded freight cars in 10 hours. Their specialized talents are always available to serve the nation in time of emergency.

The muscle-bound seatrain, easily toting cargoes too outsized for other carriers, is one of a growing sorority of seagoing ladies designed for strange cargoes.

Take the SS *Angelo Petri*, a ship that made seafaring history on her first voyage. Though never destined to bear combat arms like the redoubtable *Seatrain Texas*, she carries a cargo often more welcome

This tanker carries 67,000 tons of ore or 447,600 barrels of oil

than weapons to beleaguered troops. The $7,000,000 *Angelo Petri* is America's first wine ship. The 22,000-ton ship looks from the outside like many another tanker, albeit a spotless one, but inside she is new clear through. He 2,500,000-gallon cargo rides in 26 chromium-nickel stainless-steel vats. Every valve and pump, every foot of piping, is stainless. Cofferdams surround each vat on top, bottom and sides, so 26 different flavors of wine can be kept separate, with never a drop intermixed. Ships are naturals for wine transport, according to president Louis Petri, because their gentle motion keeps air, the greatest enemy of wine, from mixing with the cargo. As each vat empties, a twin-nozzle device lowers into the tank and jets a high-pressure steam-and-water blast on the interior.

Fruit Industries recently placed in service the SS *Tropicana*, the world's first bulk orange-juice tanker. Ultimately she'll hold nearly 1.5 million gallons of the yellow nectar in tanks pillowed with 6½ inches of foamglass. This insulation, plus vacuum-packing the juice at 2½ pounds below atmospheric pressure, delivers the tasty cargo at a frosty 30 degrees F. with flavor intact. She pumps 22,000 golden gallons per hour, surely the fastest anybody ever poured orange juice out of a can. The cheapest, too; her $15,000 tab for bringing a load from Florida to New York compares with $265,000 to do the same by refrigerated truck.

The *Marian P. Billups,* whose profile resembles a souped-up hot rod with the hood off, carries butane, propane and ammonia for the

Tropical Gas Company at the unheard-of cargo-tank pressure of 250 pounds per square inch. Her belly is crammed with 18 enormous steel bottles whose domes poke up through her deck like cylinders of a gigantic marine engine. The *Billups* would be an economic cripple for conventional cargoes but, like the bumblebee, who flies nicely despite aerodynamic theory, this 13,000-barrel gas carrier is supremely efficient for her special purpose.

Another useful "oddball" is the 590-foot *Duncan Bay*, rated a tanker but carrying the world's oddest liquid cargo—wood pulp. Other ships bring down Canadian pulp in dry bales, but the *Duncan Bay* pumps it aboard in a watery slurry like thin quicksand. When she discharges, propeller agitators whir away in the tanks like giant eggbeaters to keep the pulp mixed. In addition to speeding cargo handling, papermen say wet pulp makes stronger paper.

Some tankers still carry oil, of course, but even among oilers there are specialists. With the new SS *Cities Service Baltimore* it's variety. No smutty black-oil workhorse she; her gleaming tanks simultaneously handle 10 grades of "clean products," two grades of lubricating oils and —just to keep her hand in—1800 tons of black. She can pump off all of these varieties separately in 15 hours.

Then there's the *Alatna*, first tanker built from the keel up for Arctic operations. Put in service to supply far-north military outposts, this 300-foot bruiser can keep the seas under the most rigorous polar-weather conditions. Her hull is girded by a waterline armor belt of high-tensile steel, and she has the crushing bow contour and beefed-up rudder and props of an icebreaker. Her rugged steam-de-iced cargo gear works in high winds at 65 below zero. Her lightweight aluminum lifeboats have attached runners for ice travel. She has an elevated heliport on the poop deck aft, fitting her for the increasing use of helicopters in Arctic operations. Down below she carries sleds, track-type snow vehicles, Yukon stoves and Arctic survival gear.

This 530-foot wine tanker is the first ship of its kind under U. S. flag

Pan Atlantic Steamship Company's *Ideal-X* was born a tanker, but you wouldn't know her now. Bethlehem installed a full-length upper deck on which she piggybacks 58 loaded trailer bodies, each carrying a 40,000-pound load. The company has installed special unloading equipment at New York and Houston that makes this hybrid ship highly profitable.

Mightiest of the tankers-plus, and a new idea threatening to outdate present bulk-carrier fleets, is the big SS *Sinclair Petrolore*. This 790-foot giant is an oil tanker going and an ore carrier coming, her novel design licking the empty return trip that steals bulk-carrier profits. Largest tanker afloat from her christening in November 1955 until the mammoth *Universe Leader* took that honor a year later, she remains the world's largest oil-ore carrier. She makes an oil run from the Persian Gulf to Marcus Hook, Pa., then to Venezuela to load ore for Japan, then full circle to the gulf—a 91 percent payload run compared with the usual 50 percent.

The immense Niarchos tanker building at Bethlehem Quincy Shipyard will be the world's largest. This 940-foot colossus with a 106,500-ton dead-weight will heft an unbelievable 825,000 barrels of oil and can steam nonstop around the world. She'll scrape bottom in a 50-foot channel, rendering obsolete harbors around the world and necessitating offshore lighterage at many ports—but the load of oil she totes makes it all worthwhile.

You wouldn't recognize the lowly wartime Liberty ship these days. The Maritime Commission's experimental *Thomas Nelson* had a face lifting that replaced her cargo booms with mechanical cranes that purr across the deck on geared tracks. This is the general-cargo ship's first new look in half a century. (Incidentally, streamlining her seacow shape with a 20-foot extension and repowering with black-oil diesels raised her from a lumbering 10 knots to 17½, and gives our vast reserve Liberty fleet a new strategic value.) Another Liberty, dubbed simply *Yag 40*, has a huge "bird bath" perched 60 feet high atop a slender king post in which she collects the most elusive cargo ever manifested —radioactive dust from atomic explosions. She steams ghostlike through the test area by radio control, with no one on board. For lower-level tests she can be controlled from a watertight cubicle in the center of a flooded cargo hold (for shielding), wherein the skipper can see television pictures transmitted from the engineering gauge board and from a trainable camera on the mast. The USCGC *Courier*, a Liberty turned seagoing broadcasting station and equipped with the most powerful transmitters of their kind afloat, relays the Voice of America behind the iron curtain. And Liberty *John L. Sullivan* is propelled by four Pratt and Whitney T34 airplane engines mounted on deck. This is to test the practicability of an air-propeller-driven cargo ship without vulnerable underwater propeller and rudder for use in mined or debris-laden waters.

THE GLACIER CARVES a dock in the bay ice of McMurdo Sound. With her 21,000-horsepower engines, she crushes a form-fitting berth in the 12-foot ice

Antarctic Album

PM Editor Richard F. Dempewolff found a good many vivid hues when he visited Antarctica with Operation Deepfreeze. Here are some color scenes from the bottom of the world

BLUE GROTTOES in crevasses of the Antarctic are beautiful, but dangerous

YOUR GRIZZLED CORRESPONDENT wore a beard to avoid painful shaving with snow

SEVENTY-FIVE-FOOT radio towers still stood at Little America I, but only eight feet remained uncovered when we visited the 1928 site with Admiral Byrd

ANTARCTIC SUNBATHING is the popular recreation for seals during the subfreezing summer. Some varieties weigh 500 pounds

SOUTH POLE HOUSING—*antique and modern sit side by side at Hut Point. In the background are prefabricated homes of the air-facility camp for the expedition. In the foreground is the house erected by Scott in 1902. It is now filled with snow*

I'M THE MAYOR *of this place Admiral Byrd told us when he arrived by helicopter at the ice-prairie site of Little America I. Cameramen record his visit. In 1955 a 220-mile chunk of his desolate domain broke off and went into the sea*

LONELY CROSS *erected by the British still stands on a peak at Hut Point, commem-
orating heroic journey of Scott and four of his men. They died returning from pole*

IN A HUT *we found a meal left by
Shackleton party in 1917. Preserved are:
1. Coffee; 2, 3, 4. Biscuits; 5. Scale and
cake; 6. Potatoes; 7. Candy; 8. Bread;
9. Cheese; 10. Photo chemical; 11. Wine;
12. Camera back*

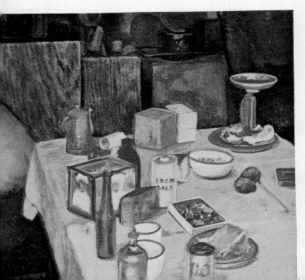

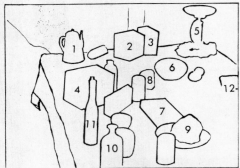

BOY MEETS GIRL

BOY GETS GIRL

PLUS A DIVIDEND

AND FAMILY RESPONSIBILITY

On a volcanic ridge in Antarctica we found 35,000 Adelie penguins enjoying family life. Extremely sociable, they greeted us each day, apparently thinking us to be big penguins

WORKHORSE VEHICLES *for snowfields are the tracked Weasel, left, and the Sno-Cat, right. These two, painted orange for quick spotting, are loaded for the trail*

SWIMMING IS *fatal in the 28-degree polar sea, though these experimental immersion suits may stretch life expectancy from eight to 35 minutes*

HOW STRONG *is the floor? South-polar-bay ice melts from the bottom, so regular checks are necessary*

LIGHT TRAIL *party heads out across 600 miles of storm-swept ice to find a site for scientific observation camp*

DEEPFREEZE PARATROOPERS *have four legs. The expedition's dog teams are used for rescue and survival work. They are dropped by parachute, along with sleds*

RELIC OF ANTARCTIC *history is this hut erected by Shackleton at Cape Royde in 1908. Tons of food cached around the building are well preserved. We drank cocoa and ate jam and cheese that had lain in this open freezer for nearly 50 years*

PROBING ELECTRONIC *hand on the front of this Weasel is a crevasse detector un-der test. It signals the driver when it passes over a snow-bridged chasm*

HOME SWEET *home to these dog drivers was a tent. The temperature stayed below freezing from the knees down, but sometimes was 40 degrees at head height*

FAREWELL TO ANTARCTICA *was marked by an emergency visit to Little America V to unload a search plane to look for survivors of a crash. The cliffs are 25 feet high here*

Amid a deafening racket
and a putrid odor,
New Zealand is taking
much-needed

Power
from
Man-Made
Geysers

By Richard F. Dempewolff

Mud lakes near Wairakei steam and bubble

You hear and smell Wairakei long before you get to it. The sulphurous breath of Hades hangs in the picturesque valleys of northern New Zealand's uplands—fuming from hundreds of boiling mudholes, steaming pits and fissures in the earth's crust on the Waikato River plain. Here, more than 40 shrieking manmade geysers are sending white jets of steam billowing hundreds of feet up and across the scalded valley floor. The ground trembles and the noise is deafening. The landscape is dusted with pumice and crusted with heavy white deposits of silica. Trees kissed by those infernal jets glitter like white-sprayed Christmas decoration. They soon become dead snags under the heat and the fumes.

Wairakei lies in the center of a vast thermal region stretching 170 miles northeastward through villages with colorful Maori names like Tongariro, Waiotapu, Rotorua and Tikitere. In Rotorua, boiling geysers have ripped through the floors of stores and sent hot mud 25 feet into the air, steam puffs from gutter drains, asphalt streets develop hot patches and the golf course boasts unique natural hazards—small open steam vents that grunt puffs of vapor and are known as "grunting pigs." Homes and public buildings get their hot water and heat from shallow wells. One resident grows orchids in a greenhouse heated with geothermal steam.

None of this is new to the Maoris, who have been using the subterranean steam since A.D. 1500 to cook their food, wash clothing and bathe. But neither Maoris nor British colonials who followed them were aware, until recently, of the full potential of the forces beneath them.

At Wairakei, hard-hatted crews are drilling through the earth's crust to tap nature's boiler for the high-pressure, superheated steam. Already it is turning generators to produce electrical power for northern New Zealand's growing domestic and industrial needs. Mr. L. Fooks, energetic superintendent of the Wairakei Geothermal Project, explains that the $12,000,000 job of turning volcanoes into volts is not just a frightening experiment. "We've about reached the end of North Island's hydroelectric potential," he points out, "and coal-fired power stations are impossibly expensive here. But now we've got ready-made steam power without any fuel cost. Right here in Wairakei there's a proven potential of 250,000 kilowatts—and it may even go to 500,000."

No one on the project knew what he'd be getting into when the first bores were drilled at Wairakei in 1949. Sulphurated hydrogen is combined with the steam rising from vents in the Tongariro and Rotorua areas. Last year two ditch diggers in Wairakei village collapsed and died from fumes. "We could and did take precautions against fumes," says Fooks. "But our biggest hazard was from blowouts—and still is. Underground vapors are still forced up through fissures in new places. They turn the country to scalding mud that undermines buildings and drill rigs. So far we've been lucky." The first 4-inch test hole struck

Steam from a "cleaned" well is deflected into horizontal pipes and shoots hundreds of yards across the countryside

The local Indians guide the warm water into pools for laundry and bathing

hot water at 200 feet. Thirteen others were sunk to depths reaching 1100 feet. One produced a steam jet capable of spinning a 1000-kilowatt generator, and the engineers went on to deeper, wider holes. The largest hole, a 10-incher, came in with enough steam for 6000 kilowatts. But the granddaddy of them all was an 8-inch bore that geysered in to the tune of a potential 20,000 kilowatts of power.

Drilling is accomplished much the same way an oil-drilling crew brings in black gold in Texas or Oklahoma. In fact, the drilling rigs came from Oklahoma. Water and mud are poured into the hole as the drill grinds down, and pulverized rock is washed out periodically. No one knows exactly when the hole will "blow." Any bore more than 200 feet deep may suddenly send everything sky-high, Fooks reports. "We control them by pouring cold water down the hole while drilling. An 8-inch column of water in a 1000-foot stand of pipe exerts enough pressure to hold the steam down for a while." These holes must have much more substantial wellheads and valving than oil wells. No less than 100 tons of concrete are poured at the wellhead to hold the pipe steady when nearly one million pounds of steam and water per hour come gushing through it.

Drillers know that things are about to happen when the bottom temperature begins to soar and the mud coming out of the hole is boiling. Even when drenched with cold water, bits come up searing hot from bores that log temperatures from 300 to 500 degrees F. Underlying "base" rock is estimated to run between 1300 and 1800 degrees F. The ground for miles around thunders and shakes when a bore comes in. First out is a towering cascade of water—and everyone runs for cover. Steam mixed with mud spews from the hole to heights of 500 feet or more. With an explosion like the boom of heavy artillery, the fireworks begin. A roaring cascade of red-hot rocks is fired skyward like a small volcano. The rocks explode in mid-air with a high-pitched crackling noise as they emerge to atmospheric pressure. The eruption may last for days. "When our first 6-inch bore was uncapped," recalls Fooks, "she spewed rocks and debris 600 feet high for more than 2 days, kicking 500 cubic yards of material out of the earth's innards."

More recently, a 3000-foot bore shot hot pebbles and pumice skyward for three days. The temperature at the bottom of the hole, just before the drill train was pulled, measured 512 degrees F. The steam came at a pressure of 400 pounds per square inch. Most of the bores at Wairakei go down 2000 or 3000 feet, with wellhead pressures of about 300 pounds per square inch wide open. Wellheads are capped with massive valves that are opened when a bore comes in. The hole is permitted to spew vertically until it has blown itself clean; then the top valve is shut and the steam is diverted to a horizontal pipe with a muffler on the end. After tests are made, it is shut down to await connection with the 20-inch insulated main line that will feed it to the generators. "One 8-inch bore," says Fooks, "came in with such tremendous pressure we couldn't shut the valve. It may have been damaged by rocks during the blowout. Men, working with ears plugged and muffed, had to go into the wellhead pit and weld a new 10-inch section with a heavier valve over the open hole."

Backgroundwise, our planet's core is believed to be a white-hot mass of matter called magma, with temperatures soaring above 7000 degrees F. In most places an impervious crust of rock and sediments 50 miles thick insulates us from this furnace. In a few places, however, the crust is weak and still "settling." Great cracks form. Through these cleavages, magmatic masses are squeezed upward. As pressures lessen, the magma liquefies into lava, which may burst through to the surface. If so, a volcano is born. More often it is trapped deep in the crust, and the proof of its presence is seen in volcanic steam, geysers and hot springs. Steam also may come from surface water seeping down through fissures until it reaches the lava, where it is superheated and driven up by its own pressure. Many scientists believe there is also a "magmatic steam" from water in molecular form which is present in rocks and actually may be part of the magma itself.

No two wells are likely to produce exactly the same type of steam. Nor it is "pure." Wairakei's steam is laden with hydrogen sulfide, carbon dioxide, silica, salt and "wetness." Wet steam with impurities will corrode turbines quickly, so New Zealand engineers have had to pipe their steam through "U" turns that whip off some of the water, then feed it through centrifugal driers to remove the rest. "It's an expensive, complicated process," Fooks reveals, "but it still gives us power at about one cent per kilowatt, about the same as hydropower and half the cost of using coal."

Already steam enough to develop 100,000 kilowatts of power is roaring away in Wairakei's smoky valley. Two rigs are working around

This vast sulphur deposit was created by escaping steam

the clock, each putting down an eight-inch bore every six weeks. Each bore is producing steam capable of turning up another 5000 kilowatts of electricity. Next year, the initial powerhouse will start pumping 140,000 kilowatts into northern New Zealand's power lines. What makes New Zealanders happiest is the "continuous load" factor. Unlike hydroplants that drop to 60-percent capacity in dry seasons, or coal plants affected by strikes, volcanic steam goes screaming along at 100-percent capacity year in and year out. Furthermore, Wairakei is only one little 2-square-mile area in that 170-mile-long volcanic trough. Engineers know that dozens of other hot spots will prove equally suitable for power production. "We don't believe from what we've seen so far that the supply is exhaustible," says Fooks.

New Zealand is not the first country to use volcanic-steam power. Right after World War II, engineers developed a tremendous volcanic-power project at Larderello, Italy. Today, some 150 wells produce enough dry steam to develop more than 15 percent of all Italy's electrical power needs. Engineers at Larderello have found it necessary to keep drilling new wells, since the volume of steam does decrease, not because the infernal steam is giving out, but because fissures in the earth become caked with deposits from the steam and gradually choke off. New wells drilled within 100 yards of old ones come in with original force and volume, and have no effect on the volume of the old well nearby. With the supply of volcanic steam available, the electric station can generate 260,000 kilowatts of power. Also, in an effort to conserve chemical products in the steam, Italian engineers have recovered about 30 tons of sulphur daily. The steam is passed through dry boxes to remove carbon dioxide and hydrogen sulfide. The sulfide is reduced to elemental sulphur with iron oxide, and sulphur is extracted with carbon disulfide.

Mexico too has parties in the field, investigating hot springs on the high central plateau under the shadow of Popocatepetl. Exploratory drilling with the cooperation of a United Nations technical-assistance program has resulted in a successful bore in Hidalgo, 80 miles north of Mexico City, and plans are proposed for a 25,000-kilowatt generating plant. Volcanic energy programs are gaining headway in the Central American republic of El Salvador and on Britain's Caribbean island of St. Lucia. In Iceland—volcanic isle of fire, ice and virtually no fuel—subterranean steam has been used by inhabitants for 25 years to heat most of Reykjavik's homes, buildings and swimming pools.

In this country, the Magma Power Company has announced that a test bore has been drilled by them in the Big Geyser area of California, 85 miles south of San Francisco. What came out of that hole set Magma to work on the first such power plant in the United States. If everything goes as planned, California soon will have a 100,000-kilowatt generating plant, operating wholly on volcanic steam.

Here sulphurous steam roars through a valley, killing the vegetation

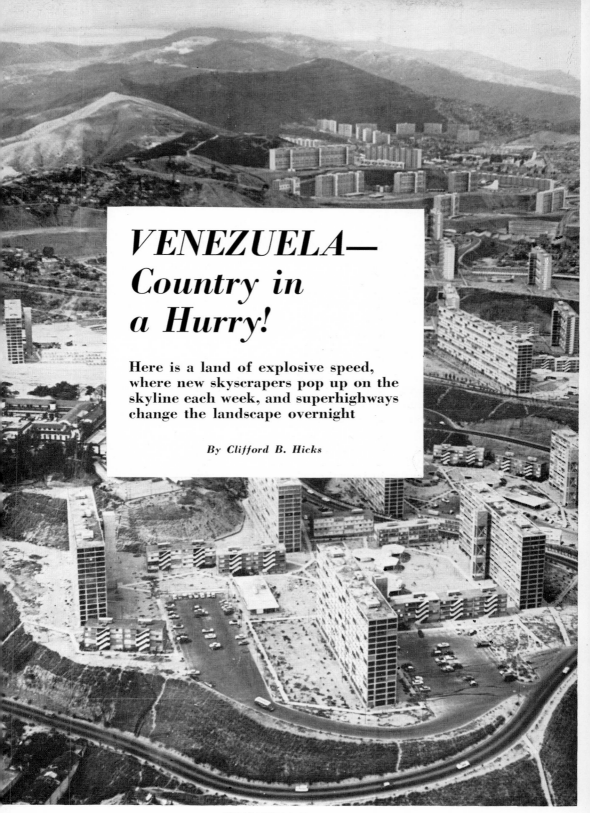

VENEZUELA—
Country in
a Hurry!

Here is a land of explosive speed, where new skyscrapers pop up on the skyline each week, and superhighways change the landscape overnight

By Clifford B. Hicks

Venezuela is a land of violent contrasts—a land of incalculable wealth and widespread poverty, of breathtaking skyscrapers and slum shacks by the thousands, of superhighways and trackless jungles.

But most of all, Venezuela is a land of explosive speed. Venezuelans are determined to lift themselves from the ox cart to the jet age within the span of a single generation, come internal political turmoil or pressures from the outside world.

You can see the results of this determination everywhere. You watch the ageless, deep-etched face of an Indian woman as she moves her meager belongings from a mud hut to a magnificent apartment on the 15th floor of a baby skyscraper. You stroll through one of the world's most modern and beautiful universities with a student whose cousin, deep in the interior, lives a hundred miles from the closest elementary school. You watch Jaguars by the dozens wheeling along the Autopista, and at the same moment, deep in the jungle, a naked Indian is stalking his kind of jaguar with a blowgun.

Venezuela also is the land of the incredible statistic, for only statistics can show the magnitude of the people's efforts to raise themselves to the jet age overnight. Venezuelans love to quote statistics to prove the magnitude of their effort. Here are a few:

In the short span of 10 years, 200,000 people will have been moved from shacks into magnificent apartment buildings.

A huge complex of chemical factories, built in less than three years, soon will be turning out 180,000 tons of fertilizer per year (more than three times Venezuela's own requirements) along with plastics, synthetic rubber and industrial chemicals.

In just 18 months, thousands of workers and machines toiling day and night moved more than 15 million cubic yards of dirt to build what Venezuelans say is the world's longest earthen dam, a dam that stretches for nine miles and will irrigate 300,000 acres of now-arid land, boosting livestock production by five times in central Venezuela.

This picture was taken in August, before construction of new road was begun

In central Caracas, the 400-year-old capital city, more than 400 buildings were razed to build a magnificent commercial center. Already $90,000,000 has been poured into the center, and the total cost eventually will reach $300,000,000 if the original plans are carried out—compared with $100,000,000 for our own Rockefeller Center. In 15 years Caracas has been transformed from a sleepy overgrown village of 300,000 persons to an exciting metropolis of more than a million.

In just 12 months Venezuela completed more than 1000 public-works projects costing some $500,000,000. In five years more than $2,000,000,000 have been spent on public improvements.

And Venezuelans seem determined to maintain such staggering statistics, come what may. Following the revolution of January 1958, a junta of military officers and civilians took over the administration of the national cash register. One of the first acts of this group was to announce:

"We intend to maintain a high level of public construction, placing emphasis on projects that are essential, such as railroad, harbor and highway improvements and development of new petrochemical and steel industries. Showplace projects such as fancy hotels and monuments, which often were pushed by the last administration, will have low priority."

Venezuelans are well on their way to their goal of lifting themselves by their oil derricks overnight. Gone are the ox carts around Caracas. Today the new Autopista, a six-lane superhighway, is jammed with Thunderbirds, Cadillacs, Jaguars and Imperials. For centuries the University of Caracas struggled along in the same ancient buildings. Today, with facilities for 7500 students, it is one of the most beautiful and modern universities in the world, boasting all spanking-new buildings within a period of four years. In the mountains above Caracas a 3000-kilowatt atomic reactor soon will yield nuclear energy for scientific research.

In December, four months later, a beautiful four-lane highway was completed

Here the Pan-American Highway enters Caracas

The annoyances of high-speed civilization, of course, go hand-in-hand with the benefits. Radios in Venezuela spout endless advertisements, and Latin-type ducks squawk singing commercials from television screens. In downtown Caracas, prior to the revolution, you had to drop the equivalent of 30 cents into a parking meter for just one hour's parking. (It may be significant that as soon as the revolt was touched off, parking meters were ripped out by the dozens!)

Throughout the populated sections of Venezuela there is a throbbing urgency to tear down the old and build up the new overnight. A stop watch could well be the national symbol. You see construction gangs working 'round the clock everywhere. Nightfall is the signal only to turn on the huge floodlights. Standing on any of the hills of Caracas, you are surrounded by small armies of men working on projects of breathtaking scope. And, except for the remaining slum shacks, a majority of the multistory buildings within your view have been built within the past 10 years. The sight is electrifying and in a way terrifying, for you wonder how the patient peasants of Venezuela can adapt themselves to this resounding environment of clanging bulldozers and thundering concrete mixers.

Fortunately Venezuela can afford the pace of its progress. It is, indeed, a land of fantastic wealth. Again, only statistics can tell the story. Oil production has doubled since 1950, and now can run as much as 2,245,000 barrels per day. Venezuela is the world's largest oil exporter, and second only to the United States in the production of crude. And the ground will continue to gush this black wealth for years to come, for Venezuela has 16 billion barrels of proven oil reserves, six percent of the world's total.

Down in the wild interior of the country are several vast deposits of iron ore estimated at well over two billion tons. In 1957, iron-ore production increased by a third to 15 million tons. Pockets of gold, precious stones and valuable minerals pockmark the trackless jungles. Many areas have not even been prospected.

In Venezuela, despite changes in government, it's not a question of whether to spend for vast public works, but how best to spend the money that's pumped up by the oil derricks. In one recent year, 57 percent of the budget was set aside for public works. So far as is known, no other government in history has spent more than 30 percent on such projects. (Another sizeable whack of the budget has gone to equip the armed forces with the latest weapons including jet planes.) Part of the 57 percent for public works went into highways, industries and other projects essential to the economy. Another part went into the tremendous housing projects for lower-income workers.

But a substantial share also went to "showplace" projects, designed for the most part to impress the rest of the world. A dozen tourist hotels of unbelievable opulence, built and operated by the government, are strewn across the country—but relatively few tourists check in, and many of the magnificent suites stand empty. At the time I visited the Hotel Humboldt, perched atop a 7000-foot mountain and accessible only by cable car, I spotted only half a dozen guests in a building which would put most other hotels throughout the world to shame. The Armed Forces Club, for sheer splendor, would outrank the pleasure palaces of ancient Rome. And at the very moment of the revolution a year ago, workers were putting the finishing touches on a spectacular $50,000,000 racetrack.

It's a safe bet that the current administration in Venezuela will not emphasize such showplaces. However, projects necessary to a sound and diversified economy, as well as those of value to lower-income families, will be continued. Venezuela is a land of the poor and the rich,

This modern building is typical of the ultramodern architecture of Venezuela

with very little in between. Its people now seem determined to use the gushing oil and mountains of ore to improve the living standard throughout the country—and do it at an incredible pace.

Particularly is this true in Caracas, the nation's capital, and other large cities. As you ride through Caracas, bizarre and richly colored skyscrapers on every side give you the feeling that you are riding through the city of tomorrow.

Consider the matter of housing. For decades, workers in Caracas have lived in tiny shacks of mud or scraps of wood, carved into the mountainsides. Sanitary facilities have been nonexistent, and water has been toted up steep slopes in tin cans.

Then came the world's biggest slum-clearance project, completed in three leapfrog phases.

In the 1955 phase, bulldozers rumbled into action, scraping away the entire side of a mountain. By the first of July the site was cleared and ready. From then on, the speed of construction was unbelievable. By the second of December, 13 magnificent apartment buildings, each 15 stories high and 10 apartments long, complete with elevators, were ready for occupancy. Many four-story apartment buildings also were built. Workers from an area of concentrated slums quickly were moved into the 2366 attractive and spacious four and five-room apartments.

Immediately, bulldozers moved in to smash over their former homes. Again in 1956, by the first of July, this area of slums had been cleared and was ready for construction. By December, 16 new apartment-sky-scrapers were ready for occupancy. As soon as these were occupied, more vacant shacks were razed to make room for the third project. It was completed in 1957 and consists of 20 super-apartment buildings. The speed of construction is phenomenal on such projects. There are three shifts of workers, thousands of men to each shift, and the buildings actually appear to grow, floor by floor, overnight.

Six more 15-story blocks are under construction. Other housing

It's a happy day when a peasant family moves from the slums to a new apartment

Slum areas are rapidly being replaced by modern apartments

projects are under way both in Caracas and in other cities, but Venezuela admittedly has a long way to go to clear its vast slum areas.

The buildings are daring, both in design and appearance. For the most part they are sparkling white, but huge panels, painted at random in bold hues, produce a stark and colorful effect. Sections of construction tile, set on their sides, make a lacy mosaic up the sides of the buildings. These open tiles form the open walls of the apartment kitchens, providing air conditioning in a climate that approaches the ideal anyway.

Nestled around the tall buildings are schools, theaters and shopping areas, all built simultaneously with the apartments. And there's a whole series of "beisbol" diamonds, for baseball is the national sport of Venezuela, too. (In fact, baseball is almost a cult. The banner headline on the front page of one of the Caracas newspapers during my visit concerned the record of Saturnino Orestes Minoso, better known as Minnie throughout the beisbol-playing world.) The huge new baseball stadium in Caracas seats 35,000 spectators, and there isn't a post to obstruct your view in the entire structure.

By 1960 the existing skyscrapers of Caracas will be overshadowed by a new building still more daring in design and unique in concept. This 25-story structure will be built in a spiral around a mountain. The "Helicoid" or "spiral in space," built with private funds, will cost $25,000,000. Already the miniature mountain has been bulldozed into the shape of a cone with a spiral up the side. When the Helicoid is finished, shoppers will be able to drive up a spiral road right "through" the building, and shop on both sides of the ramp.

Venezuelan architecture, bizarre in appearance, features sheer walls, elaborate mosaics and panels painted in brilliant colors. For the most part, the new buildings have skeletons of reinforced concrete. Curtain walls of concrete block or glass are built up around the skeletons. This type of construction, along with the highway-building program, has produced a soaring demand for cement. The ideal occupation in Venezuela would appear to be that of a cement salesman. The largest cement company in Venezuela is raising its capacity from 2780 to 4600 tons *per day!*

Auto traffic, that bane of the high-speed world, is causing growing pains in Venezuela, too. Caracas, like a jewel in an exquisite setting, lies in a beautiful mountain valley only nine miles from the seacoast, but the elevation of the city is 3000 feet. A mountain range intervenes between the city and the coast. Five years ago the only access to the city was via a perilous two-lane road that wound for 21 miles and 365 curves through a spectacular but dangerous spur of the Andes. Accidents were common, and an accident could well send you tumbling down 1000 feet of the mountainside. Today you can travel the six-lane Autopista from the coast 11 miles into the center of the city, where you pick up another superhighway that slices through central Caracas, dipping right under the two 30-story towers of Bolivar Center.

Southeast of Caracas 300 miles, in an area that was virtually uninhabited a few years ago, a huge new steel mill is rising that eventually will provide 1.2 million tons of steel annually. Nearby, on the turbulent

Sisal is one of the major products of rural Venezuela. It's used for rope

Caroni River, electricians are putting the finishing touches on the powerhouse of a new dam, 165 feet high and 1165 feet long, which will power the steel mill. At present it is turning out 50,000 kilowatts, but this will eventually be expanded to 300,000.

Over in the northwest corner of the country is Lake Maracaibo, one of the richest spots in the world because of its oil. The black gold, for the most part, lies in pools under the lake. Oil derricks punctuate the surface of the water like so many stakes marking off the plat of a real-estate development. Thousands of men are at work building a $100,000,000 bridge across the lake, a bridge that will be carefully studied by engineers throughout the world, for it will be one of the longest prestressed-concrete structures ever built.

Throughout modern times, Venezuela has been forced to import a significant part of its food requirements. Now, thanks to a coordinated effort to solve the problem, Venezuela is raising 85 percent of its food. Farm lands rapidly are being upgraded through fertilizers and irrigation. Agricultural research and education are providing better crops and larger harvests. Twenty-one agricultural colonies have been established. In some respects the colonists remind you of our own settlers during the homesteading days, for colonists are given an opportunity to "prove up" or pay for their land. Homes, tools, seeds and schools are provided. As the settler brings in his crops, he uses the income to buy his land and home. At Turen, biggest of the colonies, 600 farm families are harvesting corn, beans and sesame in an area that produced nothing a few years ago.

Improving the country is almost a bootstrap operation because of the former level of education. Even today, about half the population is illiterate. But the current administration has ordered construction of 223 new schools, and school registrations today are double what they were 10 years ago. Thousands of illiterate adults are awkwardly learning to hold pen and pencil as they squirm through classroom sessions at night

Venezuela raises 85 per cent of its food. Here natives harvest a pineapple crop

Oil—here being pumped from beneath Lake Maracaibo—is paying for the change

in an effort to educate themselves comparatively late in life. You can't build a new country without learning how.

Venezuelans, perhaps, are proudest of their petrochemical plant. Three years ago the 750-acre site was nothing but untouched jungle and swamp. Overnight more than 3500 workers moved in with their families, built themselves a community and started erecting buildings. Today more than 20 huge factories dot the landscape and 10,000 people are living in a city that didn't exist three years ago. Already the plant is turning out fertilizer by the hundreds of thousands of tons, and soon it will produce plastics, artificial textiles, explosives, insecticides, synthetic rubber and vital industrial chemicals, all made from petroleum.

One thing you can't escape in Venezuela is the smell of fresh paint. If a stop watch could serve as an appropriate national symbol, a paintbrush could well be the great seal of the land. Everywhere you go you see Venezuelans wielding paintbrushes. Many of the jerry-built slum shacks are painted in clean, bright colors. Down along the seacoast I spotted a man giving the trunks of a whole grove of palm trees a coat of gleaming white paint. When I asked him why he was painting the trees, he thought a moment and replied, "Because they told me to." Then, gazing down the rows of white pillars, he added, "Looks most beautiful, doesn't it?" It did, too.